Er

"This is a deeply provocative book taking one on the emotional roller coaster ride of the victim of severe sexual abuse as a child and the therapeutically calming carousel ride of her occupational therapist. The book raises very salient questions related to the efficacy of the traditional application of therapeutic techniques and media and poses some challenging tensions between theology and psychology. It also provides a valuable insight into the differences between being "scientifically therapeutic" and being " spiritually therapeutic". It particularly addresses the critical role of spirituality in therapeutic applications and the absolute essentiality of addressing the "soul" component in the psyche, soma, soul totality of the persona, and particularly how the soul component of the persona takes control to bring about healing.

While it is a gripping account of the protagonist, Hazel's, journey to healing, I cannot say it is an easy read. It is never easy to read the deeply intimate, disturbing and, painful consequences that such abuse has upon its victim. But it is a very positive book in its demonstration of the healing effects brought about by the inter-relatedness between loving and supportive relationships, our own creativity and our Creator and how these links can become a powerful therapeutic tool that transforms us from victim into victor.

Both authors are to be congratulated on their courage in sharing this profound, experiential journey with us and its potential to become instrumental in changing our approach to our therapy and our relationships with those we serve.

Although written within a Christian ethos, the book addresses spirituality and the human soul from a universal perspective and would thus be meaningful to anyone regardless of religious affiliation."

Associate Professor Robin Joubert
Nat.Dip.Occ.Ther.
(Pretoria),BA(UNISA),MOT(UDW), D.Ed(UKZN)

"This outstanding resource, co-authored by a therapist and her client, introduces a unique, innovative approach to healing from trauma. The healing process documented here is fascinating, instructive, and compelling; it moves beyond traditional, narrative psychotherapeutic approaches by seamlessly and effectively integrating the creative toolkit typically utilized in occupational therapy. The creative work of the client, so evident in this beautiful book, provides a powerful complement to this beautifully woven narrative of healing."

Laura Davis, author of *The Courage to Heal* and *The Burning Light of Two Stars*

"The emotions, uncertainty, and isolation expressed by the author in this book, are the same ones experienced by those of us, who have gone through a similar experience. It is reassuring to see the practical ways described in the book that can help those of us who are not bold enough to open and share publicly. I found this book down-to-earth, and it has been written in layman's terms, so I could relate to it and understand it better than if it was written for professionals. Captivating from the first words, I am sure this book will help many people who are feeling alone and lost."

Anonymous survivor of sexual abuse

"Hazel and Louise's remarkable account of a very special reciprocal relationship, is a "tour de force." It is quite unique in its level of deep complex concepts and academic content. Basic to the core of this book is the statement "True healing cannot occur if the spiritual aspect is not incorporated into the healing process." Spiritual aspects of occupational therapy have been addressed occasionally by theorists and authors over the years but never quite to this depth and extent. Being so very open, with excellent description and intriguing theoretical detail, have made occupational therapy and occupational group therapy in this field come alive. From Hazel's perspective it shows what good therapy can achieve.

I would like to mention 3 very specific features of this book that stand out for me and need special mention, especially for occupational therapists who would be fortunate enough to read this book.

Firstly, the reader will be aware that Louise's availability to Hazel was very flexible. She was there for her at the most important times. One of these was when they were locked out of the house and sat on the bench in the garden.

Secondly is the concept of intuition, which is very special, and relates to how well an occupational therapist is aware of her/his own reactions and the effect on the therapeutic relationship. Louise questioned herself in the book, but I have experienced her as being an occupational therapist with great insight and intuition, and the spirituality shines out of her. Thirdly one must note the skill with which Louise used activities such as painting, clay modelling and cards to absolute perfection in her intervention. What a wonderful example for us as a profession.

Lastly, I must make mention of Hazel's courage to be so open and to share her healing process with us. It will have an impact on many people."

Dr. Rosemary B Crouch
Professor of Therapeutic Sciences at
the University of Witwatersrand

"There are so many incredible experiences of human suffering and triumph in this book. Coupled to a profound desire to turn some of those mental and emotionally challenging issues into genuine desires to reach out to as many people as possible who could benefit from your combined life's experiences.

Having been on the St Raphael's Sanctuary retreat, I stand by you as you make a success of guiding people to healing in the Lord and sowing the seeds of hope. Referring to a quote from your book "If your soul is dying…" I see the need now, more than ever before, to reach out to people who are truly suffering and who experience great problems at every twist and turn wherever they live out their lives of modern human endeavor. Never in the history of our human existence have we experienced such an overwhelming pandemic of challenges and threats to our very existence."

Reverend David Anderson
Diocesan priest of the Archdiocese of Cape Town

Too Close to Remember

Lived Experiences of a Client and a Therapist on a Psycho-Spiritual Journey of Healing

Hazel Zion and
Louise Fouché

Published and distributed in the United States
by Spiritual Biz Publishing, Inc.

ISBN XXXXXXXXX

The author of this book does not dispense medical advice, or prescribe the use of any technique as a form of treatment for physical, emotional, or medical problems without the advice or guidance of a physician/therapist, either directly or indirectly. The intent of the author is only to offer information of a general nature to help you in your quest for emotional, and spiritual well-being. In the event you use any of the information in this book for yourself, the author and publisher assume no responsibility for your actions.

Library of Congress Cataloging-in-Publication Data
Names: Louise Fouche, author.
Title: Too Close To Remember / Louise Fouche
Description: 1st Edition. | Asheville, North Carolina: Spiritual Biz Publishing, Inc., 2021
Subjects: Psychology | Spirituality

Spiritual Biz
PUBLISHING

The publisher for authors dedicated to shifting consciousness.
For more of our products visit SpiritualBizPublishing.com

ACKNOWLEDGEMENTS - HAZEL

First and foremost, I am indebted to my family, without whom this book would never have been possible. To my husband – thank you for your endless patience and for creating time for my writing amidst a busy family and work life, as well as providing endless technical support and advice along the way. To our son Joshua – thank you for opening the door for me to my own healing journey, and thus helping me to transform pain into positive purpose. To my brother Mark and his partner Karen – thank you for always believing in me, often more than I believed in myself, and for your unconditional love and support throughout my journey of writing this book.

To Louise – thank you for your endless love, spiritual wisdom and professional skills in providing and holding a space for me in which I was able to heal. Also, for your ongoing encouragement, support and inspiration over the five years of writing our book together. In being yourself, you provided me with a mirror that reflected my own ability to reconnect with and embrace my most powerful tool of healing – my spirituality.

To the many authors whose autobiographies about their own trauma and healing have inspired me to find the courage to write about my own journey of healing – Fiona Doyle, Dave Pelzer, Rina Theron, Albert and Zandre De Villiers, Judith Kelly, Louise M. Wisechild, Elizabeth Smart, Linda Caine and Robin Royston, Anchien Trotsky, Irvin D. Yalom, and Ginny Elkin.

To my friends – thank you for all your supportive WhatsApp messages, words of wisdom, tissues for my tears, and immediate help with Joshua in times of crisis. You have all been a light that kept me going through some of my darkest times.

To Clyde Broster and Sonja Shannon – thank you for all of your help so freely given with the editing process and for having faith that our book could be published.

Finally, I want to mention those who were responsible for my trauma and pain – without you in my life, I would have had no reason to write this book, to find healing and, most importantly of all, to finally embrace my life's purpose.

DEDICATION - HAZEL

To our son Joshua, who has shown us the meaning of unconditional love and has shown us that healing is always possible,
regardless of how long the healing journey may take.

To everyone who has been a victim of sexual abuse in
any form – I hope our book helps you to find courage, strength and faith in your own ability to heal.

ACKNOWLEDGEMENTS - LOUISE

I am indebted to my mentors who were instrumental in igniting my passion for psychiatry and groups, and in shaping my knowledge and skills. In many ways, this journey started with them. Thank you, Rosemary Crouch, Vivian Alers, Marianne de Beer, Erla Venter and Hendrien Nortje.

To all my students who challenged me and through whom I refined my ideas and techniques. In particular, Jana Nieuwenhuizen, Adri Badenhorst and Rina Groenwald, who were willing to venture out with me, to explore new techniques and to exchange experiences.

Thank you also to all the therapists who attended my workshops, who through their vulnerability allowed us all to share in sacred moments and believe in something bigger.

I would also like to make a special mention of Hazel Zion, Heidi Morgan and Natasha Biddulph for their support through dark times, and for their honest feedback .... At times, a new road taken can be a lonely one.

To Riaan du Toit for the endless conversations, for being a home away from home, for the challenges to dream big, and for all the sacred moments shared.

Thank you to my sister, Sonja Shannon, for sharing your talent with us and for your well-thought-through guidance with the editing process.

To my mother and my brothers, Albert and Eric, who have journeyed with me through the calling of the Healing retreat and have been willing to take a leap of faith with me.

To my husband, Francois, and my children, Michael, Antoinette and Phillip – I am so grateful for the sacrifices you made during the times when I was away from home presenting workshops and conference papers. It was your love that held me and always called me back home.

DEDICATION – LOUISE

To God, my loving Father, for whom my
heart beats and my soul yearns.

CONTENTS

PREFACE

Hazel

Stuck on a Metrorail train in 2015, I intuitively found a piece of paper and a pen and started writing. Soon before this, I had discovered a long-lost piece of writing, dating back to 1994, that finally confirmed for me that I had been sexually abused as a child. Being delayed on the train, I started to reflect on the emotional turmoil of my life. As my pen started moving across the paper, I seemed to enter another world. Although I was not fully aware of it at the time, this was a world in which my soul started to speak through the words on the page. I somehow knew that I needed to keep this piece of paper and that something much more would come of it, in its own time.

Over the next eighteen months or so, I added a few pages here and there, and always felt tremendously inspired after writing. However, I struggled to find time to write, between working and being a mother. Frustrated by the lack of time, and feeling emotionally exhausted, I carefully placed my scraps of paper in a plastic folder inside a book and left it in a safe place. Finally, in August 2017, the seemingly impossible was made possible. My husband's improved income allowed us to employ someone to look after our son, and my dream of returning to my writing was fulfilled.

During the process of writing, my emotional turmoil caused long delays in completing chapters. I feared becoming over-whelmed by my feelings, and during the most difficult times, my writing would stop for a week or so while I tried to gather the emotional strength to continue. At times, I contacted Louise (my therapist who was the witness to my healing and the co-author of this book) by phone and let my tears flow while I spoke to her. This helped me to release the pain so that I was able to continue writing. At other times, I tried to follow Louise's advice to simply write down what I was feeling, regardless of how it seemed to interrupt the flow of the story. Somehow, the story at that point needed to be about where it was taking me, emotionally, in that moment. Writing in solitude in this way, I was able to transform my pain into powerful healing, releasing my tears to flow into the words I was writing. As you journey with me through my book, you will find sections in which I share my emotional journey of writing. I have tried to be true to my own healing process and to reflect it as an integral part of my story.

Throughout my journey of healing, there were times when my mind and my body were my greatest enemies. My mind screamed with doubt and my body was filled with anxiety. The essence of my healing lay in discovering my own ability to reconnect my mind, body and soul through a combination of meditation and medication. The process was complex and slow, but at the heart of it, I discovered my soul – that part of myself that was able to provide me with a channel to a wider source of wisdom and strength. I learned that it is vitally important to listen to and trust the soft, whispering voice of intuition, as difficult as it may be at times. This voice is the voice of the soul, and it can re-connect us to the immensely powerful, universal source of healing. All we have to do is to ask and be open to receiving, without specific expectations.

My truth had its own language, mostly spoken through my body and my unconscious. My unconscious spoke spon-taneously in the form of dreams, and during counselling and healing retreats it spoke through a range of projective activities, including painting, drawing, free association writing, left- and right-handed journaling, clay sculpting and working with the sand tray. These techniques provided a channel through which my unconscious voice could be heard and later understood. They enabled me to embark on my return journey towards finding, and finally healing, a lost part of myself – my abused inner child. I believe that these techniques are some of the lost jewels in the crown of a multi-disciplinary approach to therapy. They enabled me to bypass my defence mechanisms and reach a level of deep, transformational healing, which more traditional, narrative therapy approaches had been unable to achieve. It was in opening up to my soul that I finally had a means for my unconscious voice to be heard. I could finally reach and hold onto God's safety net of divine wisdom, strength and peace. Creativity, especially writing in its different forms, has enabled me to express my unconscious pain, and later to transform my pain into healing.

My final journey towards facing the pain of my own sexual abuse was initiated through my unexpected and at-times-overwhelming emotional reactions to our two-year-old adopted son, Joshua. I can now reflect on how Joshua placed me on the road towards the most important healing journey of my life. I have come to realise that he has mirrored my shadow and has enabled me to start the process of integrating it. At the same time, in supporting his healing, I have healed myself and have found my soul purpose: to heal others. Often, our children are our source of healing. All we need to do is to listen to them with our soul.

As I write, I live with many unanswered questions regarding my abuse. However, I believe that our souls are much wiser than our minds. Some questions will remain unanswered until we are ready to move naturally into the answers. We do not necessarily have to have all the answers in order to find healing and peace.

I hope that this book will be an inspiration to you and others travelling on similar journeys, in knowing that there is always another side to pain – healing. I now know that healing is always possible if we are prepared to embrace the pain and to find a channel through which we can transform it. I wish to plant a seed of hope in your heart that there is light, both within and after the pain and darkness, and that you too are able to heal.

Finally, and most importantly, I would like you to know that touching my experience through reading my story is only a starting point. Jennifer Ross, author of *Isaiah's Story*, said: "Sharing your brokenness helps others heal in their own brokenness." It is my hope that, through sharing my brokenness with you, I can help you to find healing in your own life.

PROLOGUE

Louise

Seeing is believing. In the Bible, we read the story of Thomas who says to his fellow disciples, "Unless I see the nail marks in his hands and put my finger where the nails were, and put my hand into his side, I will not believe" (John 20:25). After Jesus appears to Thomas and then allows him to place his fingers in His wounds, Jesus ends by saying, "Because you have seen me, you have believed; blessed are those who have not seen and yet have believed" (John 20:29). After journeying with Hazel for the last four years, I have come to the conclusion that those who believe will see. Ah, and what a sight to behold!

My own journey of discovery and healing is inextricably linked with Hazel's journey. This journey of mine started more than twenty years ago. I became more and more aware of the two seemingly opposite fields of theology and psychology. My experiences as a therapist led to more questions than I could answer. Psychology focuses on the self and encourages egocentric behaviours such as setting boundaries and being assertive, while the Christian faith focuses on loving others and encourages behaviours such as forgiveness, self-sacrifice, and even loving one's enemies. Psychological principles infused my treatment sessions, yet it felt like I was facilitating principles that seemed contrary to my faith. In my occupational therapy sessions, I was teaching my clients skills like assertiveness and establishing boundaries, which I considered to be self-centred. My Christian faith was advocating loving others and even loving your enemies or those that wronged you. I found it increasingly difficult to facilitate principles that were not supported by my faith. Could these two important approaches be married in any way? If they could, what would it look like and did occupational therapy have a role to play? Finding the answers to these questions led me on a twenty-year journey. I believe that Hazel was sent on my path for the last four years of this journey, to help crystallise the thoughts, feelings and beliefs that had started to emerge. This book hopes to highlight these elements for you through Hazel's story.

I remember the first time I met Hazel. She was volunteering at the Old Age Home in our local town, playing games with the residents in her spare time. I needed a carer/volunteer to assist in implementing a maintenance plan for a client, and the matron suggested that I contact Hazel, saying that she was "good". At that stage, Hazel was working at one of the guest farms as a receptionist and was close to being fired, having been given her last warning. She struck me as someone who had lost parts of herself and was floating; knowing there was something more, but not knowing what it was. She had started the process of adoption after IVF attempts had failed and had left her devastated. She came across as reserved and, in some ways, hesitant. As our journey started, she asked whether I would be able to assist her with a counselling course she was doing, as she wanted to become a counsellor, seeing that she had a social work degree she wanted to fall back onto.

In summary, our journey together brought me to the soul. I believe that we are all made in God's image and we all have a soul. I have found that the soul, which can be described as a conduit for God's Spirit or presence, or His voice, is the core of our being. The more in touch and aligned we are with the soul, the more we can tap into a Divine wisdom. At some stage in our lives, we stopped listening to the soul. Healing happens with greater ease, almost naturally and intuitively, when we reconnect with the soul and listen to its wisdom. This does not mean that our lives become smooth and problem-free, but it makes our lives more meaningful. Even more importantly, it provides us with incredible strength (or weakness, if that is what is needed) to live our purpose in the world, despite incredible hardships, as Hazel's life testifies. Without becoming too technical and theoretical, which we feel is beyond the scope of this book, I will explain the thoughts, feelings and beliefs behind the different parts of Hazel's experiences. I will also reflect on my memories of Hazel's sessions and her transformation. Throughout this book, I will make reference to God, Jesus and the Holy Spirit during my own reflections, as my Christian faith is what I know and who I am. Hazel has used other terms like "spirit" and "guardian angel". In the past, I have facilitated sessions with atheists, agnostics, esoterics and people of various Christian denominations. The point is: We each have a soul. I encourage you to look past the definitions and labels; they can be debated another day. Find your own soul-truth. Try some of the exercises (which you will find at the end of each chapter) for yourself and reconnect with your soul. Your soul will point the way that you are to journey.

Throughout this book, you will become a witness to Hazel's incredible story of healing and finding purpose despite brokenness. You will see the strength of supportive love. Hazel's story is not unique and, even though the details of your life may be different, you will find yourself in these pages. May you take courage from Hazel and start stepping into your own life, believing your own truth and being amazed by the wonder and the beauty of God, our Creator, who constantly calls us and loves us into life.

1

ME AND I

Hazel

My first few years in life were marked by primal trauma which strongly influenced the way in which I made sense of my world later as an adult. When I was born, I was sent straight to a foster family where I spent my first 18 months. My biological mother was not coping with the three children she already had, my three older brothers and had left my father. A social worker became involved and my siblings were sent to either a children's home or another foster family. My family was torn apart even before I came into the world.

My foster mother had asked to adopt me, but her decision was overturned by the Social Worker after my biological mother returned to my father. In South Africa family reunification is always seen as the priority. I had already bonded with my foster mother but was then torn away from her at 18 months and placed back with my biological parents. This move was deeply traumatic for me. As my biological parents had their own personal problems and pain, they in turn failed to bond with me. Maybe, unconsciously, this laid the foundation to me wanting to become a psychologist and social worker.

My healing journey started in 1994 when I was a twenty-four-year-old Psychology Honours student at Rhodes University. As a young student of Psychology and Social Work, I had a burning desire to change the world through applying Critical Psychology approaches based in community work, and to rescue all the underprivileged children in the world through my role as a Social Worker.

I was in psychotherapy at the time, having been struggling with ongoing depression and anxiety. Looking back, I realise that my first clear memory of depression had in fact first emerged when I was a teenager in high school. It then re-emerged a number of times as a young adult and then again around the ages of forty and forty-three.

Upon deeper reflection, I see that my depression entailed experiencing a deep feeling of "hollowness" inside of me – a sense that at the core of my character I was somehow intrinsically bad and unlovable. I felt like a rotten apple that no one would want to eat. I saw little purpose in living, as I had nothing of value to offer anyone. I thought that I was rotten on the inside and felt powerless to change that. Initially, as a means of trying to compensate for this, my self-esteem became dependent on my achievements. I became highly self-critical and had very high expectations of myself, becoming a bit of a perfectionist. I struggled with performance anxiety and constantly compared myself to those who had achieved more than I had. I shone academically at school and placed myself under great pressure to be highly successful in everything I accomplished. I now realise that, to this day, I still carry this tendency with me to some extent, although it no longer defines me.

Further than experiencing these feelings of being rotten on the inside, I deeply disliked being female. I refused to even be called a girl when I was younger – I was a boy! I had almost no sexual interest in men until after the age of twenty, and I believed that I was sexually unattractive. I chose to express myself as being asexual, always wearing very loose-fitting, sexually neutral clothes that completely hid my slim, feminine figure. Furthermore, I completely neglected my personal care. I succeeded in making myself look sexually unattractive, which was how I felt. I now recall being attracted to a male student friend who I subsequently discovered was homosexual. This pattern was repeated in my first marriage when my husband realised that he was homosexual. I always just assumed that that was the way I was born and that, having had three older brothers, I would always be a "tomboy". I had no idea at the time that, on a deeper unconscious level, I had completely suppressed my own sexuality. There was a childhood link to my depression, anxiety and sense of being asexual, and these spoke of repressed sexual abuse.

It would be more than twenty years before I would begin to make sense of the language of my unconscious mind as it spoke to me through dreams, as well as through a wide range of creative techniques in occupational therapy and, most significantly, through various forms of writing.

Most of my early childhood memories involved my brother Mark, we were very close. As a young teenager Mark was sexually abused by his choirmaster at the church where he was a chorister for a period of about 4 years. Tragically, his abuse was actively encouraged by my mother and Mark was told by my mother to leave the family home when he finally found the courage to put a stop to the abuse at approximately 18 years of age. Mark then moved out and rented a private apartment.

It was around the time that Mark left that I discussed with a teacher at my high school what had been happening at home. Nothing could be proven as Mark had not told anyone about what had happened other than my parents at this stage. However, I carried this immense rage and I was like a bomb about to explode on a short fuse. I just knew that I didn't want to be living under my parents' roof anymore. My teacher then facilitated my move into a Children's Home where I stayed from the age of 16 to 18, until I finished school.

Some of the fondest memories I have of Mark involve the acting shows we presented at home, at local Old Age Homes and at churches. We were innovative, using old broken sheets as curtains and even having a collection plate for donations towards the next show. The show that remains engraved most clearly in my memory now, more than thirty-five years later, is the show about the Christian crucifixion story, which we presented at the Spiritualist church that we attended as a family. Mark played the role of Jesus and I played the role of Mary, his mother. We were the only two characters in the show. What has stayed with me, to this day, is the very real sense of sadness I experienced when he died on the cross. It seemed as if I was no longer playing a role, but rather experiencing a premonition of what was to come in his real life.

My deepest struggles seemed to emerge on two levels – both the unconscious level and the conscious level. On a conscious level, I fought a spiritual battle, being torn between Christianity and Spiritualism. I knew that the source of this battle lay in my early childhood exposure to both religions. On the unconscious level, my fight was with my personal chronic depression and anxiety. However, I was completely lost in the dark with this, having no sense at all of its cause or source.

My spiritual struggles had their roots in my childhood. The earliest spiritual influence in my life was the path of Spiritualism. My parents followed the path of Spiritualism at the time, and the Sunday school I attended was run by my father. However, I also remember later, as a teenager, being involved in a youth group run by a local Christian church and finding some level of emotional support through a few of the good people I met there. For a brief period of time in my later high school years, I even identified myself as a born-again Christian, which must have offered me a sense of hope and social belonging, which I so desperately needed at the time. Furthermore, I recall attending church services at the Anglican St George's Cathedral where Mark was a young chorister. I also attended Spiritualist circles and séances with my parents and a few of their friends. I remember that my siblings and I all had pictures of our guardian angels, drawn by psychic artists, hanging in our bedrooms. I never knew what to fill in on forms that asked about my religious beliefs or which church I attended, so I always defaulted to Methodist, thinking that was the safest option.

As my spiritual and personal battles intensified, there were times when I felt that I did not want to live with myself anymore. At times, I felt completely overwhelmed, just wanting to end everything, including my own life.

I now realise the significance of the crucifixion show that Mark and I presented in the Spiritualist church. Christianity and Spiritualism interpret the meaning of the crucifixion very differently. Spiritualism does not believe that Jesus' death paid the penalty for our sins. As such, his death on the cross does not carry the atoning value in Spiritualism that it does in Christianity. My memory of the show signified that my upbringing had left me confused on a spiritual level, hanging in limbo in a grey territory somewhere between Western Christianity and Eastern philosophies, including Spiritualism.

As a young adult, I shifted completely towards Eastern philosophies and a total rejection of Christianity. This shift was largely fuelled by the realisation that Mark had been sexually abused for years by his choirmaster at a local prestigious Anglican church. Furthermore, my critical mind could not accept a lot of the Christian teachings. As a young adult, I attended local meditation groups and briefly explored a range of Eastern philosophies including Buddhism and Hinduism. While not identifying specifically with any one of these philosophies, I felt more at home with them than with Christianity.

I began to explore meditation, as well as the therapeutic transpersonal psychology technique of Holotropic Breathwork, in a practical workshop when I was a Psychology Honours student. Holotropic Breathwork is an intense breathing technique that uses short, intense breaths followed by long, deep breaths. This brings about an altered state of consciousness, transcending the ego state of awareness.

I also felt strongly drawn to alternative psychology theorists such as Jung, and transpersonal psychology, which incorporate a spiritual part of the self as being fundamental in the healing process.

I had begun my new journey of self-awareness, and my awareness of there being two parts of myself – the "I" and the "me" – started to grow. "I" did not want to live with "me" and my personal and spiritual struggles anymore. "I" seemed to be aware of "me", but I was unsure of which part of me was the "real" or "true" me.

This book is about how my journey through the pain of my own repressed sexual abuse has re-connected me with what I have always known – that the "I" is my True Self or soul and the "me" is my False Self or ego. Somehow, it has taken the most painful journey of my life to be able to trust my own answer to that question; an answer that I have always known. The journey towards finding this answer forms the heart of my writing of this book, and it is interwoven throughout all the chapters.

I wish I knew more about you, who you are and where your travels in life are taking you, as I share my story with you. I sincerely hope that you, too, will be able to journey towards answering these questions for yourself, allowing them to heal you. Regardless of what resolutions are found or left as unanswered questions, what I can testify to, is that healing is always possible, no matter how long and how hard the journey.

Your soul has always known how to heal.

READER'S REFLECTION:

Do you ever have a fleeting moment of relative peace while caught up in a storm of difficult thoughts – a peace that brings a sense of a little distance or space between you and your thoughts? You may not be able to explain or understand where this sense of peace comes from, but you sense it strongly, if only very briefly. Now you may be wondering how you can reconnect with this momentary peace. Try to make a little time in the day to meditate. Start by breathing and focusing your mind only on your breathing and your bodily responses to breathing. When your thoughts interfere and you start to identify with them, don't fight them. Rather just gently try to re-focus on your breathing and let your thoughts come and go, as if you are watching leaves on a stream floating past you. If, like me, you really struggle to find undisturbed time in your day, you can try to do this while you are doing mundane daily chores like washing up or ironing.

2

THE START OF MY
JOURNEY... WAY BACK

Louise

I remember it so clearly, as if it were yesterday: the day when I could no longer deny that there is a divine wisdom that is present in all of us; that wants us to be healed. I was presenting an occupational therapy group session at a private psychiatric clinic. The group consisted of about eight people who had conscientiously attended and participated for almost two weeks. The group was working hard, but it seemed as if there were still so many unanswered questions and so many decisions the clients needed to make before they were to be discharged. It was a Thursday morning, and I was at a bit of a loss as to the theme and the activity I should choose for the session I would facilitate. I wanted to facilitate the decisions that needed to be made; decisions like: "Should I return to a previous partner who has been unfaithful?"; "Should I return to my job in which I was over-stressed and unhappy?"; and "Where am I going to find the strength to cope with my cantankerous boss?" Although different sessions had been presented around these themes over the previous weeks, my clients had stalled and avoided answering the questions. At times, the group hovered superficially, not daring to go deeper. Their answers were glib, as they had not really owned them. They were typical self-help book answers, with nothing authentic to them or their situation. Mentally, I was trying out all the different approaches and activities to find a fresh approach; the one that would be the key to unlocking their fear of taking that crucial step. I silently whispered a prayer, "Dear Lord, help me to help them." Suddenly, I remembered an activity that I had used previously with a group of therapists, during which one occupational therapist had said to me, "It felt like it was my soul talking to me."

I walked into the group setting, wondering how my clients (most of whom had been diagnosed with major depression and different forms of anxiety) would react to the instructions. The cohesion in the group was strong and, before long, I laid out a variety of pictures and asked my clients to choose one picture that resonated with them; the picture that jumped out at them or moved them, even if they couldn't consciously explain why. I took them through the instructions step-by-step, reminding them to move away from their mind; not to think, but to allow a letter to flow through them onto paper. A sacred atmosphere entered the group as each client wrote down the most beautiful, authentic insights of their own personal problems; letters filled with incredible depth and wisdom. I was struck at how these insights differed from the glib answers given previously and how some clients' "answers" were not what therapists would have expected; yet the answers were perfect for each client's personal situation. When everyone had finished reading the letters, there was silence in the group – as if the group was grappling with what had just happened. Slowly, the clients started discussing the realisation that a part of each of them had known the answer all along, but that they had stopped listening to their own soul, their own inner divine wisdom. Aside from the incredible letters, the realisation that the group members possessed this inner wisdom was priceless. At that moment, my own anxiety about their discharge vanished.

Once anyone finds their own divine wisdom, their connection to God, something irreversible happens inside them.

According to my training, from a psychological framework, I would have had to define the activity as a projective technique in which the unconscious was made conscious. I had worked with the unconscious before in projective techniques, but it was mostly fraught with anxiety and aspects of shame or guilt. The innate quality of the letters written revealed love, support and wisdom. None of the characteristics of anxiety, shame or guilt were observable in the clients themselves or in any of their answers. What happened in this group session was something totally different. I could no longer deny that the Holy Spirit and God need to be essential elements in therapy for clients to be healed; not cured but healed. A piece of the puzzle was falling into place and I started asking more questions: "If we could facilitate this process in our therapy, how different would the therapeutic process and the outcomes be for our clients?"; "Could these insights be facilitated more easily and, if so, how?"; and "Would the changes be more sustainable?"

Although this group session was a turning point for me, my journey with divine wisdom (theology) and psychology had started long before then. I can't recall the exact order of events, but I will touch on the most important aspects that shaped my questions and thoughts around these two frameworks; frameworks that initially appeared to oppose each other in essence.

In 1984, when I was in Std 6 (Grade 8), Rosemary Crouch, an internationally known occupational therapist, came to our school on career day with a slideshow explaining occupational therapy. Instantly I knew, with a deep inner knowing, that I would be an occupational therapist; I never doubted it and never looked back. During my training, I was confronted with views and perspectives that were not upheld by my Catholic faith and beliefs; for example, people were encouraged to divorce if they were in abusive marriages, and sterilization was encouraged for people with intellectual disability. I watched as friends and fellow students went to psychologists and became so assertive that they pushed others out of their lives. The focus of treatment was on the individual and seemed to enforce egocentricity. My view of helping others was labelled as "rescuing" people, and my lecturers silently shook their heads – it was clearly a no-no. I was told that I was compensating for my poor self-worth; helping others to make myself feel good. I was told that people were to be encouraged to "live their own lives" and not succumb to the archaic rules of institutional regulations or religion. We were told never to mention God or anything religious or spiritual during treatment, as it was against the guidelines of the Health Professions Council and meant that we were enforcing our views on others. When a client mentioned God, we were meant to steer them away from Him and focus on the treatment at hand. We were not to pray with clients; this was to be left to their pastors or family and friends. In order to live and work within this new and foreign paradigm that clashed with my beliefs, I followed the rules at work with clients and then tried to return to my way of living my faith on a daily basis when I was at home. Initially it seemed to work, but who was I kidding? I became more and more confused and started querying both paradigms. I knew I had to resolve the contradiction, but I did not know how.

After qualifying as an occupational therapist, I worked at the Adolescent Unit at Weskoppies Hospital. There, having just returned from a psychodrama workshop with enthusiasm, and being young and courageous, I decided to try some of the psychodrama techniques. We had admitted a young adolescent boy with oppositional defiant disorder to the unit, because he refused to cut his hair and his school had suspended him. At a loss as to what to do with him, his parents had had him admitted. So, there we stood in the psychodrama session and the scene playing out in front of me involved this boy, whom we'll call Walter, going to ask Axel Rose (yes, way back from Guns & Roses), Walter's hero, why he had long hair. Walter chose another boy in the Unit, let's call him Ben, to play the part of Axel Rose. My heart skipped a beat. Ben! This was going to be a disaster, and how was I going to explain this to my team? I started to panic. Ben was not the brightest boy in our group, and he often made inappropriate comments due to his poor insight. In the therapeutic drama, Walter went up to Ben, posing as Axel Rose, and said, "So, Axel, why do you have long hair?" I held my breath. Then he answered: "This? No, this is only a wig," and he motioned as if taking the wig off. Silence fell. Walter frowned and stared. In that moment, I stood totally mesmerised and in awe of the wisdom of the group. Never in a million years would I have given that answer; neither would anyone else in the group have said that. The right person, at the right time, gave the perfect answer. The story has a great and crazy ending: that night, Walter asked Ben to cut his hair, and he was discharged that Friday. It only took one sentence to totally change Walter's perspective.

The incident made me realise the wisdom of the group: collectively, the group members seemed to connect with each other on a deep level, which allowed them to access a divine wisdom not accessible to the average therapist through conventional methods. Realising this, I started listening with different ears to the support and advice that the group members freely offered each other. The more I listened with ears for divine wisdom, the more I picked up the golden nuggets of precious insights shared. I observed that, more often than not, groups that had strong cohesion provided group members with a safe environment – no, more than that – a sacred environment, in which they could take risks, moving away from their egos and becoming truer to themselves. The connection and interaction that took place in these sacred groups had a different quality. It was as if the group members now felt safe enough to look themselves in the eye, to find their own power and to courageously make life-changing decisions. Yet, not all groups were able to reach this deep level, and I wondered what I as a facilitator needed to do to enhance this process.

Another experience that assisted me on my journey arose from two books that I read that stayed with me long after I had finished reading them. They added fuel to the fire of my already confused state concerning psychology and/or theology. The first book was called *A Child of Eternity*, and it was authored by Adriana Rocha and Kristi Jorde. In a nutshell, the book was about a child with autism who was provided with an alternative communication system. Through the answers she gave to questions about complex issues in the world, the child showed extraordinary wisdom. Being a practising Catholic and not subscribing to the New Age themes that emerged throughout the book, I didn't take it to heart initially. Then a question caught my eye: "What do you perceive psychosis to be?" The answer was: "Sickness of the spirit; sickness of the spiritual body." Despite not having bought into the story whole-heartedly, for some reason I couldn't shake this answer. I started asking my own questions: "Is this why there is currently no cure for schizophrenia?"; "Is this why so many of my clients have some form of religious hallucinations or delusions?"; "If this is true, then what would be the treatment for it?"; and "How can it be healed?"

Unfortunately, I cannot trace the title or the author of the second book. If my memory serves me right, it was written by a South African father who had lost his son in a motor car accident. The father was overcome with grief and then his son started to visit him from the afterlife. As the father was suffering from severe depression due to grief, the son said to him, "Depression is a symptom of spiritual transformation that is occurring." This was written in the early 1990s and at that stage very few medical doctors would afford any time to such claims. After all, depression was considered to be caused by a chemical imbalance in the brain. Now, almost twenty years later, more and more people are offering this hypothesis through their research, through scientific means. You only need to browse YouTube and you will find YouTube clips on this subject. One I strongly recommend is "Depression or spiritual awakening: Two sides of the same door". Again, this second book I read provided me with a different perspective. If depression was viewed as a symptom of spiritual awakening, then surely, we would "treat" our clients differently. Then depression would become something to celebrate, not to label and condemn. I can almost hear you ask, "But then, why are so many people suffering from depression?" Maybe it is because we are stopping the transformation process through using medication and a therapeutic process that looks for pathology and tries to rectify it. I was left wondering, "If this is true, how should I change my therapy: both the process and the outcome we should be striving for?" and "How does a therapist facilitate spiritual transformation?"

Although I did not subscribe to all the beliefs within these books, these perspectives mulled around in my head. For the first time, there was a hint that psychology and spirituality are linked in some way; that they are not necessarily contradictory, but that they could possibly both be part of a bigger picture, a bigger process. These ideas in turn raised more questions.

The next important stage of my journey occurred when I became a lecturer at the University of Pretoria after working in the Adolescent Unit at Weskoppies Hospital (a psychiatric hospital) for almost five years. This changed the dynamics drastically. I was no longer merely following the paradigm at work, but I now also had to teach it to new impressionable, questioning students; students who asked the same faith-based questions I was asking "at home". Yet, I was giving the prescribed answers. I found myself being the one silently shaking my head at students who wanted to "rescue" others. I saw students grappling with the same issues that I had.

In the year 2000, a new curriculum was introduced and I was the main coordinator for the mental health block for the second-year students. One specific incident that occurred during this time stands out for me. As part of the mental health block, one theme dealt with how mental illness is defined and how various religions and traditional cultures view mental illness. In order to make the lecture interesting and interactive, I invited therapists from various cultural and religious backgrounds to each give a short presentation and then to answer questions from the students. The panel was made up of a Hindu, a Moslem, a traditional African therapist and a liberal Christian. Not in my wildest dreams did I anticipate the strong negative reaction this panel would elicit from the students. So many were reiterating the beliefs I had and giving a voice to all my struggles and questions. Seeing that I was "at work", I gave the prescribed answers, but the dissonance in me became visceral. During one student rotation, we invited a Sangoma (traditional African medicine-woman) to speak to the group. Fascinatingly, she worked at a private psychiatric clinic to which many African clients were admitted. According to her traditional beliefs, some clients did not have delusions and weren't suffering from a mental illness but were rather suffering from "Ukuthwasa." Ukuthwasa was an experience that happened to all people who were called to become Sangomas but refused to answer the call. They presented exactly like patients with psychosis, and according to Western medicine would be diagnosed as schizophrenic. However, her job at the clinic was to help the clients accept their calling. Once they did, the symptoms dissipated, they became healed and they left the clinic to be apprentices to study the art of being a Sangoma. It would have been so easy to dismiss this view if it was not that the Sangoma offered to "throw the bones" for me. Highly anxious, as this is viewed as an apostasy in my church, I agreed so that I could smooth relations. In front of my eyes, the Sangoma revealed things to me about my life that she had no way of knowing. It was no longer easy for me to just laugh it off. Feeling guilty and confused, I tried to bury it with all the other nagging questions. Pressure was starting to mount.

In 2005 my life was falling apart, and I am sure that this could largely be ascribed to my being untrue to my True Self. My husband and I were going through marital strife, my kids turned to their au pair in times of need, I was still trying to deal with the grief of my father's death, and I was trying to cope with increased expectations at work while having less support. My soul was dying. My life was extended way past capacity and I knew something was going to break if a drastic decision wasn't made to change something ... anything.

My family and I took a leap of faith. My husband and I resigned from our jobs, we packed up our belongings, and we moved to a small town in the Western Cape to farm and start a retreat centre that would focus on Healing – a place where I could, in my own space and time, explore concepts of psychology and theology without being defined by the medical framework. Without going into too much detail, suffice to say that nothing turned out as planned. We "lost" the dairy cows and Parmalat, a large local dairy company, closed their milk route through our town. We needed to have an offset for our milk, so we bought a milk business in a neighbouring town. We used up all our pension money for living expenses and were soon selling farming equipment to pay for the business. In the meantime, our neighbour refused to grant permission for re-zoning, meaning that we couldn't proceed to open a retreat centre, as we shared a road servitude with him. It was when life brought me to my knees that I started to form a closer, personal relationship with God. I spent more and more time in prayer, reading my Bible, having spiritual debates with friends and family, and reading tirelessly: all literature on spirituality, insights of the saints, self-help books and Julia Cameron's series on Creativity including the book like "The Artist's way".

In order to have extra income, I worked as a locum at a private psychiatric hospital and helped to train the staff members in the interactive model of occupational group therapy. Being frustrated with the worn-out and ineffective traditional manner of presenting craft groups for mental health clients, I started to explore new, innovative options, observing the impact on clients and listening to feedback with divine ears. One more piece of the puzzle fell into place for me when I observed a man using fabric paint, during a craft session, to paint a woman. It sounds like a common practice, but this was significantly different from anything I had observed or facilitated before. The man was totally engrossed in his work. He would take some paint, blend the different shades and paint a bit. Then he would stop, take a step back and admire this painting. He continued this process over and over again. Every time that he stopped and stared, it was as if he was in another world. The only possible way I can describe it, is to say that every time he stepped back, he was doing some inner spiritual work. Observing from the outside, I intuitively felt something shift in the room. Soon other people in the craft room noticed and stopped what they were doing. They were drawn to this man – not only to his painting, but also to the process he was going through, observing his evolution. We were all mesmerised. We couldn't take our eyes off him. He carried on painting, totally oblivious of anything or anyone in the room. When he had finished, I must admit that the end product, the painting, would not have won any awards, but it was breathtakingly beautiful, because in a sense it was a dimension of his soul. Everyone gave him compliments and each person left the group a bit taller – we had all been influenced by this man's painting. Even now, years later, just recalling this incident, I am still profoundly moved; so much so that I am feeling my eyes becoming moist as I write now. How much time are we spending in occupational therapy sessions messing around, wasting time with small craft tasks? The penny that dropped was the answer to the question of the difference between creating and making. Making is going through the motions, following the steps – our bodies and minds are engaged, but not our souls. Creating engages our all: body, mind and soul. Creating impacts others around us. Creating also comes at a cost; it costs us a bit of our soul. In order to create, we place a bit of our soul into what we are creating. Yet, paradoxically, in paying the price, we and others grow taller.

St Francis of Assisi said:

"Working with your hands is labouring.
Working with your hands and mind is a trade.
Working with your hands, mind and soul is art."

After this realisation, my level of irritation with the definition of "occupation", which is the core philosophy of occupational therapy, became unbearable. "Occupation" represented such a small word, a small gesture, keeping our treatment small and ineffective. Honestly, how many clients' lives have been changed, really changed, through their craft group or through "occupation"? In all my years of work, I can honestly not count, to fill one hand, the number of clients that I think came to major insight through the traditional craft group. Should that not give us an indication of how ineffective we are? Perhaps my time as an occupational therapist had come to an end. I found it harder and harder to subscribe to the "ethos" or core of our profession. More and more, I gravitated towards "creating" as the core of my new calling.

In 2010, we had to sell the milk business and, overnight, my husband was unemployed. As a Caucasian male above the age of forty, in the era of BBBEE (Broad-Based Black Economic Empowerment – a South African policy in which black people are given preferential employment opportunities, to right the wrongs of the Apartheid system), without a suitable professional degree and without an employment history over the previous five years (other than that of running an unsuccessful business), the likelihood of him getting another job was slim-to-none. It is funny how God directs our steps. Now I had no choice. I had to become the breadwinner and had to try to return to clinical work ... as an occupational therapist. Sigh! When you live in a rural town, population 1 500, with another occupational therapy practice already established in your town, options are very limited. Thinking outside of the box was not only needed; it was crucial. By Divine intervention, Jana Nieuwenhuizen, one of my old students who worked in Schweizer-Reneke, contacted me and asked me to present a workshop on occupational therapy groups in Potchefstroom, as therapists in the area wanted to sharpen their skills. I agreed to fly up and present the workshop on the condition that all aspects of the workshop would be arranged by Jana. That was the start of OTGrow, a company training occupational therapists in group techniques. There was more interest in the workshop than there were places available, so we immediately organised a follow-up workshop in the Free State Province of South Africa, then one in Gauteng Province. OTGrow was born out of this need. It affected my thinking in

18

numerous ways. I realised that I would need to up my game. I wanted the therapists to experience the group process, in order to fully understand the power of cohesion, of universality, of belonging. In the group, I wanted the therapists to experience their True Self. In order to achieve this, I needed to plan each group session I presented anew, to incorporate my new insights and explore ways for group members to experience the sacredness of human connections and of belonging to a group.

Another piece of the puzzle fell into place when I invited Daleen Casteleijn (an occupational therapy professor) to present a workshop in Worcester. She had completed her PhD by developing an outcome-based measure that was based on the Model of Creative Ability. It was the ideal time to chat about the concept of "creating" or "creative ability". Again, I don't recall all the details of the conversations we had, but I do remember three things. Firstly, I remember that she described some research that had recently been completed by Tania van der Merwe as part of her master's degree. In a nutshell, Tania found that all careers present today can be divided into the seven philosophical areas defined by Aristotle; all, that is, except one. There was no profession or career that matched the areas of both "art" and "spirituality". There it was! Art and spirituality – the words at the core of creating; at the core of the questions I was asking; at the core of the observations I was making but could not yet succinctly define. At that point, I saw a glimmer of light at the end of the tunnel for myself, for clients and for occupational therapists. I felt that I had rediscovered the soul of occupational therapy.

Secondly, I remember feeling the flame of enthusiasm that the Creative Ability Model reignited in me. Despite all other occupational therapy models focusing on occupation, here was a model, described more than fifty years ago, that made use of concepts like "creative capacity", "creative ability" and "creative potential". Please note, this creativity is *not* defined in the conventional manner as creative thinking: thinking in new, out-of-the-box ways or the way a teacher would define a child as being artistic. No, this creativity is rather seen as the ability to create, which is defined by Webster's Dictionary as "to cause to come into being, as something unique that would not naturally evolve or that is *not* made by an ordinary process". This model was talking my language, my soul language. I pulled my old university books closer, dusted them off and started looking at the model with fresh eyes.

Thirdly, I remember that I realised that the discussions around creative ability and creating were starting to quench a thirst in me, and that I needed more.

At the same time that OTGrow was budding, our family had not given up on developing our Healing Retreat for St Raphael's Sanctuary i.e. the name of our retreat centre situated on our farm. We decided to continue developing the programme, despite not having permission from our neighbour. We felt that when the time was right, the matter would be resolved. In the meantime, we started putting everything together and giving structure to our healing programme. Ironically, my brother Albert is a Catholic priest and has studied Theology, reading without ceasing all the deep theological perspectives on healing. So, in a sense, Albert came from the theological perspective I grew up with and struggled to assimilate in my work. Having specialised in mental health in occupational therapy, and delving deeper into the psychological elements, I represented the psychological aspects I have special-ised in, as well as the new insights and experiences I had gained. In the process of our giving birth to the healing programme, we naturally amalgamated the theological and psychological per-spectives. Everything I had studied and experienced, questioned and found answers for, tried and tested, came to fruition in the programme. I will not go into detail about the programme at this stage. Part of it will be revealed in Hazel's personal journey as the book continues. This will hopefully clarify how the creative exercises are used to facilitate deeper spiritual transformations. For now, let's return to my story.

It was at this stage of my journey that Hazel entered my life. I think it is more accurate to say that Hazel was sent into my life. Little did I know at the time how our lives would be transformed by our journey. The day I met Hazel seemed quite an insignificant day at the time. I needed someone to assist in implementing a programme for a client I was treating at the Old Age Home. Hazel was a volunteer at the home and, in her spare time, went to play games with the residents. She had qualified as a social worker but was working at a guest farm as a receptionist. The Matron at the Old Age Home recommended that I use Hazel, saying she had a natural feel for the elderly. I was curious to meet her. My first impression of Hazel was that she was a "wall-flower". She seemed very ordinary, maybe even a bit bland. I was struck by the absence of a spark, or passion. It seemed as if she was floating through life. I had my reservations but, as she came with a recommendation, I decided to continue, to give her a chance. As the weeks passed, I learned that Hazel was on her third warning at her job and faced being fired; yet she was doing so well with my client. I couldn't bring the two aspects together. She was obviously very capable. So, what was the problem? Hazel told me that she had been married and divorced, had lived in England since graduating, had three jobs in England that weren't satisfying, had met and married an Englishman, and had immigrated back to South Africa, settling in our town. She briefly explained how much she and her husband wanted children, but she had been crushed by failed IVF attempts and two miscarriages. She and her husband were exploring the possibility of adoption. I felt sorry for her, although at that stage I didn't think much of it. However, in the back of my mind, there was a small voice whispering, "Don't you think you can help her? Don't you think she could gain from all you have discovered with your healing programme?" I shook it off; after all, she never asked for help and she was indirectly my employee. I ignored the voice and decided that we would simply continue our working relationship. It was easier and simpler that way.

Sometimes, we need to be coaxed onto our spiritual path. So, Hazel was brought to my attention again, divinely, about four weeks later. She approached me, asking me to help her with a counselling course she was doing at the time. She realised that her time at the guest farm was running out and she needed a back-up plan. Living in a small town, I knew there weren't many people available who could assist her, so I agreed to have a session or two with her, giving her guidelines and feedback.

Although our journey had started a couple of weeks earlier, it was a number of weeks later that marked the start of the spiritual journey. The start: Hazel resigned from her job at the guest farm. She realised that her soul was dying every day and, despite having no financial back-up, she took a leap of faith. And then the miracle happened: a baby was "found" for Hazel and Richard (her husband). There is an anonymous Indian proverb that states: "When we take one step towards God, He takes seven steps toward us". I cannot explain it logically, but when we are on our "right path", or rather our "divine path", the universe conspires to assist us. I have seen it time and time again. During our retreats, amazing long-awaited changes start happening when we not only open ourselves up to God's Will in our lives, but also take the first step in showing our intention and committing to it.

The real journey had started for Hazel. She stepped away from what was "not Hazel" and started to slowly and tentatively step into her own life. The start of a beautiful, amazing story unfolded, bit by bit. It was a journey that would bring me to more answers than I even thought I had questions for; a journey that crystallised a twenty-year search towards integrating spirituality into my profession – a journey that changed us both.

READER'S REFLECTION:

If your soul is dying, the first step in the healing process is to realise that the path you are on is not yours. You are correct in thinking that life is not perfect and that we live in a broken world with broken people, but God wants a life of abundance for us. He wants us to thrive. Suffering is a part of life and has an important role to play in bringing us closer to Him, closer to others and closer to our true selves. God did not promise a perfect, carefree life in this world. On the other hand, God does not want us to suffer merely for the sake of suffering. If your suffering does not bring you closer to God, to others, or to who you truly are in God's eyes, then maybe it is time to acknowledge that. Take the first committed step towards changing your life. What to do, and how to do it, will be discussed in the next pages.

3

GUIDELINES UNDERPINNING
THE JOURNEY

Louise

Years back, I intuitively knew that psychology leads people from an "it" to an "I". Most psychology models and theories focus on self-actualisation and self-awareness, and therefore the focal point of treatment is the "I". As can be expected when the "I" is the centre, it becomes egocentric. So I realised that, somehow, we needed to find a way during therapy to move people from an "I" to a "we". Perhaps that is the reason I was drawn to group therapy. Years of experience in group therapy gave me a ringside seat to witnessing incredible changes in people. However, still using a fair number of psychological and occupational therapy principles, I was struck by the fact that my clients still focused on themselves. Apart from the egocentric nature of the treatment, I noticed the amount of anxiety that was created, despite the new insights that were gained. Comments like, "I know I'm an introvert, so tough if others don't like me" or "I like who I am, so I am not going to do anything to please you" did not create inner peace. These attitudes often moved other people out of their lives, adding to my clients' feelings of isolation. My clients, and even myself, were constantly on a mission to work on inner flaws, to develop deeper levels of insight and to try to self-actualise. It seemed that each person who wanted to be mentally healthy needed to be constantly aware of him/herself and work on his/her flaws, and that self-actualisation is an elusive goal that keeps moving out of reach.

In early 2000, I was introduced to the work of Carl Jung. Concepts like "shadow work", "synchronicity", the "collective unconscious", the "false self" and the "True Self'" excited me. These seemed to be more in line with the faith principles I grew up with. The false self can be summarised as being our ego. The ego is trapped in this world. As children, we come into this world a hundred percent aware that we are spiritual beings. However, within the first seven years, we forget that and develop our ego, as influenced and informed by our parents or significant others. We may initially be spontaneous and exuberant, not thinking about what we say, but soon our parents will say, "You're too loud; calm down" or "You can't just say what you think; what you said was tactless/hurtful". Hearing these messages from our parents, we change our behaviour and our view of ourselves. Often our parents are well-meaning and have no intention of hurting us or causing harm. I believe that this is part of God's design. Somewhere in the first seven years of our life, we will adjust and adapt, and develop our ego. As we are social creatures, and we need others in our lives, we learn quickly to adopt behaviour that is accepted by the group.

However, the ego believes in the "self" with a small "s". It has forgotten who we truly are – spiritual beings made in God's image, which is our "True Self" with a capital "S". We have a divine heritage, but we are trapped in our human experience. We spend most of our lives believing that our ego or false self is who we truly are.

Are you living from your false or True Self?
Take the "Discover Your Authentic Self" quiz
found at www.TooCloseToRemember.com.
Our gift to you!

Our false self is blinded and held captive by ten "false Ps". They are false because we live as if they were the truth, but they keep us chained to our human experience. The ten false Ps are: pride, productivity, people (seeking approval), popularity, possessions, power, prestige, pleasure, perfection and position. For example, someone who is chained by the false P of possession will constantly want the next thing to buy, to wear, to have in their home, etc. Their ego believes that they need these possessions to enhance their life; to be happy. However, spiritual beings realise how trivial possessions are. Possessions are a means to an end in this life and can make our lives easier, but we don't need them, and they don't enhance who we truly are. People who live from a True sense of Self can live simplistic, uncomplicated lives and still maintain their inner peace, knowing that they can never be defined by their possessions. During retreats hosted on our farm, St Raphael's Sanctuary, we do an exercise where each person identifies the false P that keeps them blinded. Participants are encouraged to imagine what life would be like if each of these false Ps did not exist. By being in tune with your body and soul, you will be able to identify your Achilles heel that is trapping you. Most people have one or two dominant false Ps that have a deep influence and even drive the choices they make with their money, lives, relationships, faith, etc.

Unfortunately, being human, we could continue living in our false self for a lifetime without ever fully realising that we are living in a small world, and never making a shift to our True Self. We go on self-help courses and buy self-help books, not realising that we are enhancing our false self; that we are dressing up the mannequin. We live in our comfort zone, surrounding ourselves with like-minded people. In order for us to get glimpses of our True Self, something has to happen to us that will shake us out of our comfort zone; something that will show us that those false Ps and shackling thoughts we've lived with most of our lives are merely illusions. Take our previous example: the guy whose false P was possessions becomes bankrupt and loses his home. Initially it is the most awful thing that could happen to him. He falls into a depression, struggling with questions. However, through his suffering and by living through this experience, he comes to realise that he is so much more than his possessions. People having a "mid-life crisis" also are confronted with what they thought were truths and have upheld throughout their life, but then realise that these no longer hold true. According to R. Rohr, in his book *Immortal Diamond*, there are only two things that can help to break the shell of our ego, and they are: great love and suffering. Nothing else is powerful enough to crack the false self open.

By starting to live a life where our emphasis is on our spiritual True Self, it becomes obvious that many of our old beliefs or old "truths" become totally irrelevant. We become aware of another dimension of ourselves, others and life. We ask different questions. Being "perfect" or without flaws is suddenly a small goal. We realise that, spiritually, we are already perfect, and that nothing we can do or achieve will change who we are in our essence. Our emphasis changes and we focus, instead, on being "whole". Part of living in our ego has meant that we needed to suppress or disown parts of ourselves – remember the example of the exuberant, spontaneous child. As an adult, in order to become whole, we need to reconnect with and embrace those aspects of ourselves that we have pushed into the shadows. This is where shadow work becomes important. We realise that whatever we've kept hidden can never be of the light. In a later chapter, I will discuss shadow work in more detail, looking at Hazel's journey and experience to explain it. In essence, during therapy, we want to facilitate a process whereby people become aware of all aspects of their True Self. An important characteristic of the True Self is its deep wisdom, which becomes an invaluable resource on the path to healing. Our True Self intuitively knows exactly what we need to heal. We just need to learn to listen to it again.

If we truly believe that we are spiritual beings and that nothing can diminish us, or that we can in no way increase who we essentially are, we need to reconsider, with fresh eyes, the concepts of illness and suffering. We can view mental illness in a different light. For a moment, let's assume that depression is a sign of spiritual transformation. If we believe that, we will facilitate a different process during "therapy". We certainly don't want our clients to "recover" or be "cured" ("cure" being defined as returning the person to his/her previous level of functioning; therefore, going back to before their illness). We want to facilitate the transformation process where they will become aware of the True Self. We want to open their eyes to the trigger of depression as a messenger, pointing to a shackling thought or belief that has blinded them and kept them trapped. During treatment, we want them to connect with their True Self and learn to listen to it. We want decisions to be made by the True Self, and not the ego. The ego operates from a place of fear, while the True Self operates from a place of love and wisdom. In therapy, we therefore strive to let go of who we thought we are or need to be, to become more fully ourselves.

The metaphor I use to explain this concept to clients is that of a beautiful wooden box, made of rare wood, uniquely carved and made with love. The creator dies, and the box is sold at a car boot sale. Someone buys it, but they paint the box pink for a new baby room. Once the baby is older, the owners sell it and a teenager buys it and paints it black, pastes pictures of actors on it and flamboyantly adds glitter glue. In it, she stores all that is sentimental to her. Once her boyfriend breaks her heart, she throws it out. So, it continues. One day, a person who renovates things finds the box and decides to recover what is really behind all the layers. He takes time to lovingly remove the layers of paint, glitter and pictures, and to his amazement discovers a valuable wooden box. The wooden box didn't need to become anything; it was already perfect. We are already all we need to be. Our process entails letting go of all our layers, re-discovering who we are and coming home to our True Self.

If the above is true, this raises the questions, "How does this type of therapy or facilitation work?" and "How should clients be guided on their healing journey back home?" I acknowledge that we are still in the beginning stages of finding the answers, and some of these principles have become clearer through a process of trial and error. I will briefly list some of the principles that we have been able to identify through the journeys of Hazel and others. These principles formed the foundation for the therapeutic process, i.e. becoming our True Self on our soul journey:

- Creative activities evoke the voice of our soul. If we use creative activities correctly, we bypass the mind. We want to ensure that the mind is not involved, because this is where most of our defences reside, and mind-chatter keeps us trapped in our ego. Be careful not to merely make something; it is *not* the same as creating. Therefore, specific instructions must be provided for selected activities to ensure that the client is creating from a soul-space, accessing consciousness or the True Self. For example, our instructions begin by grounding our clients, leading them towards breathing more deeply, and then helping them to focus on their heart/soul space. From that space, we provide the instructions for the activity and again tell them to not use their mind, but just to allow their body and soul to create. This process allows the clients direct access to divine wisdom. True creating necessitates that we use our souls. When our creation is in front of us, and we look with new eyes, we experience sacred moments and profound wisdom.

- Our souls are ancient and new at the same time, with wisdom that surpasses logic. Facilitating problem-solving for a problem encountered by the client will bring the client to a different answer than facilitating a process of listening to our soul's wisdom. Soul wisdom provides not only a new perspective on the solutions but often a totally different way of viewing the problem. The soul's "answers" often show the bigger picture, and the language of the "way forward" is universal. For example, one of my clients wanted to know whether she should leave her boyfriend, and the answer she received was "True love is eternal". Can you see what is meant by reframing the question or problem immediately, and how the soul wisdom places the "problem" on a different plane of knowing? This in turn often removes the anxiety in decision-making, and the response then becomes obvious.

- Our intuition is another way in which our soul communicates with us. It holds divine wisdom if we learn to listen to it. Similarly, our soul "knows" things, even before they are voiced or reach our mind. For example, how does a driver suddenly know to slow down while driving on a quiet road one night, only to miss a drunken driver screeching around a corner, straddling the lanes? Or how do we instantly know, coming into a room full of strangers, which person in the room we will have a significant connection with? There is another example of our soul's amazing ability of knowing, that I have often included in a warm-up question with my groups: I ask the group members to select the group member who they believe "holds the key". The instruction is to select any person *without thinking* about it; to just do it, intuitively. Time and time again, when a group member becomes "stuck" in their problem or mind, I will ask them who the person is that they had selected as their "key". That person will then be asked about his/her view on the situation. I have yet to do this exercise where the person selected is not spot on with input and wisdom;

wisdom that often falls outside the box or is contrary to the logical solution or solutions offered by other group members.

- Nothing is coincidental. Our outside life or problem is often a reflection of what is happening inside ourselves. For example, if people are struggling with financial issues externally, they are often struggling with issues of abundance internally. The problems at the "top" of an organisation or country are a reflection of what happens at the bottom. For example, the leaders of a country reflect the individuals' ambitions and life views, etc.; if they did not, they would never have come to places of power, but would have been marginalised long before reaching the top. It is once again with different ears that one listens to a client's life story. This principle aligns with Jung's concept of synchronicity, where people and opportunities that are deeply meaningful for our soul journey arrive in our life. We ask the client to become more aware of this phenomenon, and during therapy we take a closer look.

- Our wounds become our redemption. If nothing is coincidental, not even the traumatic incidents in our lives, then that would imply that there is value in all our experiences, good and bad. It is said that only love and suffering bring about true change in people: change from our false self or ego to an awareness of our True Self or soul. Once the awareness of our True Self grows and we live more and more from this space of being, we can see the bigger picture and the underlying meaning of our wounds. By embracing them, they become our redemption. For example, in the movie *Into the Wild*, the protagonist goes on a long walk and then realises, despite all her mistakes including divorce, abortion and substance abuse, that these problems all conspired to bring her on the walk. On the walk, with this new insight, she chooses her path forward, which is drastically different from her previous one. Part of the new path is to tell her story to others, to help others to forgive themselves and to help them let go of their past. Her wounds become her redemption. If we truly believed that our wounds become our redemption, perhaps the levels of guilt and regret that people cling to would decrease significantly. Again, because we are spiritual beings, nothing can increase or decrease our being. Often our deepest wound connects us to our soul's purpose, as we will see in Hazel's journey.

- Illness is not just a chemical imbalance or a bacterial/viral invasion. Of all the illnesses that people can develop, why do some people develop one illness while another person in exactly the same environment remains healthy? Illness is an imbalance between our body, mind and soul. It is a message to us. We have missed the warning voices of the body, mind or soul long before becoming ill. Similarly, unless we rectify the imbalance or underlying problem, the illness will remain and become chronic. Research regarding cancer found that a significant number of people diagnosed with cancer had wished that they were dead, three years prior to being diagnosed.

- Our wounds occur within the first seven years of our life. In the majority of cases, the wounds occur within the primary family structure. Please note that these traumatic incidents are often viewed by the child as "traumatic" or "hurtful", although this was seldom the intention of the parent. For example, an exuberant, spontaneous child is being her loud self but the mother, having had a tough day at work or being stressed about an ill parent, then snaps at the child: "Oh for goodness' sake! Could you please just keep quiet. I really can't deal with you now." The child hears or interprets the message as, "I can't deal with you when you are so loud" or "I don't love you when you are loud". The child in turn believes that to get Mommy's approval, attention and love, she needs to be quiet. Wanting the approval, she adapts and develops a false self, strengthening her ego. In order to heal, we need to reclaim all parts of ourselves, embrace the "good" and "bad" parts of the self, and become whole. This process is known as shadow work, which brings us to the conclusion that "good-and-bad" and "right-and-wrong" are all very relative terms in the end.

- At this point in our sacred journey, after doing shadow work, we are confronted with our humanness and become hyper-aware of our spiritual nature and origin at the same time. Trying to make sense of our awareness of what appear to be polar opposites often increases our level of anxiety. As a response to this, we are brought to the point of surrendering to God or life or the universe, however you define it. It is our Big Letting Go, knowing that God is in love with us and that we can trust Him totally with our life. In a sense, surrendering is the last step of letting go, totally and utterly. A deeply moving moment in Hazel's journey, described in her own words in chapter 22, occurred when she surrendered in the chapel, and in her words, she talks about the God-Spirit-filled experience that left a profound impact on her. After this point of surrender, we *know* that life is beautiful and sacred, despite its pain, trauma and tragedy. We are able to hold life and relationships lightly but value them deeply; we become more conscious of our interconnectedness with others; and we develop a deep sense of inner peace.

- To find meaning and have a fulfilled life, we need to surrender to God and live our life from our True Self in service of others by using our unique talents, passions and character traits, as well as our good and bad past experiences. We strive towards living a life in union with God, doing His Will daily.

This chapter set out to briefly provide a framework on which to hang the experiences and insights within Hazel's journey towards discovering her True Self and living a more authentic life. As you read her incredible life story, listen with ears of consciousness and look at the incidents with eyes of spiritual awareness. Open your soul to be touched by the wisdom and sacredness of life, even if it initially appears to be camouflaged by "brokenness". It is through our brokenness that God's light can shine through. This light becomes the light that guides us and others home.

4

OUR FIRST ENCOUNTER

Hazel

After five years of employment as a front-of-house reception-ist at a tourist guest farm, I had become desperately unhappy in my work and had lost all sense of motivation to perform my work duties, despite being more than competent at the job. This resulted in me struggling not only with depression and anxiety but also with the real threat of a final written warning hanging over my head. I had largely lost my sense of self, as well as my sense of direction, feeling that I was dehydrated and alone in a desert, without a compass and with no sense of which direction to turn to find an oasis. However, there was a small oasis that appeared for me when I got involved as a volunteer at the local Old Age Home, with weekly bingo games, on my day off work. I loved it and felt a sense of coming home to myself at last, but I believed At that stage that there was no future for me as a carer or nurse because I didn't have the nursing qualifications and could not manage on a carer's income. Furthermore, at that time, I was emotionally devastated after nearly three years of miscarriages and unsuccessful fertility treatments. My overwhelming fear of loss of income and being unemployed had left me feeling as if I was standing on a cliff edge without a parachute, knowing that I had no option but to jump towards my almost-certain death, into the depths of the valley below.

I had finally leaned partially over the edge of the cliff and had reduced my work hours so that I could free up some time to clear the cobwebs in my head, look for alternative employment and explore my options. Very soon after changing to part-time employment as a receptionist, someone I knew asked me whether I was interested in being a program facilitator, as a lady she knew was looking for two persons to assist with one of her clients. I asked her to find out more for me and I arranged to meet Louise. When I heard about her occupational therapy programme for a resident at the Old Age Home (Mr. X), I felt a sense of home-coming – like I was starting to find my way back to my True Self again somehow. I started immediately and felt that I had found my soul's home at last, although I continued to work part-time as a receptionist for financial reasons. Mr. X had suffered severe brain injury from a car accident which had also left him unable to walk. He was now in a wheelchair for life and had been expe-riencing immense frustration and boredom and was struggling with anger management issues. This manifested as loud, random shouting episodes at those around him. My working world became split into a struggle between my soul and my mind. The more my passion about my work as an assistant therapist grew, the more desperately unhappy I became as a receptionist. The gap between these two parts of myself continued to widen every day as I flew on the wings of my soul into the Old Age Home and hobbled back behind the desk as a receptionist, holding onto my mind's fear.

My first impression of Louise has a specific memory associated with it: I was sitting amidst a group of staff members at the Old Age Home, who all had their eyes closed, and more than half of them had one hand up in the air. Louise had just started a staff training session for her occupational therapy programme for Mr. X and had asked everyone to close their eyes and put their hands up in the air if they felt afraid and/or scared and/or threatened

while working with him. Her session included role play counselling in pairs; group discussions on the specific situations staff
were having to manage with Mr. X; and finding effective ways
of dealing with these situations. What remains engraved in my
mind most clearly is that Louise's work seemed to be her passion – and this shone through her strongly while she successfully
engaged the staff through her interactive, experiential approach.
Of course, I did not know at the time that our journey together
over the next six years would consist of her, at times, carrying
me through my deepest, darkest despair towards deeply personal
healing, moving onto our writing this book together. Had I been
aware of this at that time, I probably would have defaulted to
running a thousand miles away from her. However, this lack
of awareness ironically allowed me to follow my gut instinct of
being drawn towards her, into the beginning of our therapeutic
journey together.

5

OUR THERAPEUTIC
JOURNEY BEGINS

Hazel

Our therapeutic journey together found its very earliest steps in rather unconventional territory. I remember a few rushed conversations with Louise, my supervisor, after my training to implement the occupational therapy programme, outside in the courtyard and sitting in the chairs in front of the office of the Old Age Home. As our training sessions drew to an end, I felt that I wanted to talk to her more about the mess that formed the picture of my life. I needed to find a small light at the end of my dark tunnel.

There was a counselling course that I wanted to do, and I asked Louise whether she might be able to assist me with practical training in counselling skills. I also needed help with issues around getting registered as a Social Worker to provide professional backup to my counselling training. I shared how immensely unhappy (and deeply in trouble with management!) I was in my receptionist work, as well as how tremendously anxious I was around giving up that work, due to the resultant loss of income.

We also discussed the possibility of generating more income through the occupational therapy programme in the future.

I felt that I had lost myself almost completely, especially over the previous two years of experiencing overwhelming grief in our desperation for a child. Not only did Louise feel to me like someone who could help me find the sign posts I needed to follow in order to find a new direction with my work, but I also started to become aware of a deeper sense of hope and upliftment within myself after speaking to her. She had something deep within her that was shining brightly and, although I could not identify exactly what it was, I knew with no uncertainty that it was this very part of myself that I had lost and needed to find. Louise had somehow initiated a game of hide-and-seek within me, during which she would walk beside me on a journey towards finding myself on so many more levels than just my work.

After a four-month break from seeing Louise, during which time we adopted Joshua, I returned to work a completely exhausted, nervous wreck. Joshua had had a minor operation in the hospital. Shortly afterwards Richard, my husband, a self-employed builder, had been critically ill in hospital and was finally being diagnosed with rheumatoid arthritis. I had turned myself into Superwoman, taking care of Joshua and Richard who could not walk or drive, and needed regular hospital visits, as well as trying to keep Richard's construction jobs going by acting as a taxi driver for his staff. I remember being so exhausted through stress and lack of sleep that I felt I would fall over upon standing up. As soon as Richard finally turned a corner and started on his long journey towards a full recovery, I plummeted into the depths of a major depression. Coming back to work almost felt like an impossibility for me, but it was a financial necessity!

The anti-depressants I was taking for my severe depression and anxiety were helping to get me through each day one step at a time, but I knew I needed more help, and I found myself in another unconventional setting with Louise – this time in her car parked in the parking area of the Old Age Home! We discussed ways in which to manage my anxiety around stepping into new territory, running an Activity Programme with the residents. We also discussed my general anxiety around the issues of income and not being a "good enough" mother.

I felt as if an enormously heavy weight was being lifted from my shoulders, as I grew more aware that the model of the "good enough" mother that I felt I could not live up to for Joshua was the part of myself that had internalised the message I had received from my parents. According to my definition, being a good enough parent meant being able to provide financially so that your child has the best material and educational opportunities in life to reach their full potential. A fountain of grief started to flow through me as this heavy weight lifted – I grieved for what I had never really received from my biological parents – unconditional love. As my tears flowed, the ground I had been standing on most of my life started to crack and then shift with my tears. After my birth, I had been fostered for approximately the first eighteen months of my life and had bonded with my foster mother. I was now being transported all the way back to my grief over the loss of my foster mother when I was a young baby. I realised that I could be a "good enough" mother, as she had been for me – I could love Joshua in the way that she had loved me. I realised that money is a necessity that can open doors of opportunities, but it can never buy love.

I am holding back tears as I write this now – asking my foster mother in heaven to be with me and to give me strength, so that I can let my tears flow through my writing and regain a sense of peace. The problem is that my glasses are now completely steamed up and my words on the screen are getting very blurry. However, after breathing deeply, I am starting to let it go, having cleaned my glasses ... the windows to my soul.

When I attended my training as an activity coordinator with the elderly, I felt a heart-warming sense of homecoming – my soul started to sing again. The sense of homecoming linked back to my childhood, as the train took me back to the same station that I had used to get to my primary school. I recalled hating, being disinterested in, and not being particularly good at knitting as a primary school child. I recalled that once, my grandmother had knitted all but a few rows of my jersey (woollen sweater) for me and that, at that time, I had not experienced a sense of failure with it – she had been happy to knit it for me! From that memory flowed tears of immense sadness, as I started to let go of the pattern of my critical self-judgement and the sense of professional failure that I experienced in my working life; that had not been the pattern for that jersey. The jersey was complete, and Louise was enabling me, once again, to not only see its wholeness, but to also wear it now and to let my soul sing with the elderly residents during our sing-a-longs while they knitted Joshua another one! Sadly, that jersey has been lost over time. However, perhaps the significance of its memory at that point in my life planted a seed for greater healing transformation through confronting my unconscious memories. A new and tremendously challenging chapter of my therapeutic journey with Louise was about to begin – shifting the focus from a conscious level to an unconscious level.

6

WHO IS MISSING IN THIS PICTURE?

Hazel

Figure 1
Drawing from my childhood scrapbook
To see the color version of this image, go to
www.TooCloseToRemember.com

My memory of re-discovering the picture (shown in Figure 1) in my personal childhood scrapbook transports me back more than twenty years. I was clearing out my personal possessions from my parents' house and found it amidst the cobwebs in the top of a cupboard. On paging through the treasured memories in the scrapbook, my hands started shaking and my heart started racing after I had turned the book upside down to see this picture. My legs turned to jelly and the world around me briefly became like a surreal, slow-motion movie picture. While I put one foot in front of the other, I felt a fleeting sense of becoming disconnected from my body, as I watched my feet moving. My feet could have been someone else's feet. I knew I needed to get away from the house and back to my friend's house. Somehow, I managed to do this and to reconnect with some level of calmness within me by the end of that day.

The picture remained deeply engraved in my mind, silently creeping like a shadow into my moments of silence and solitude, refusing to let go of me or to leave me with any peace. Over the next twenty years, it found its way to three different therapists at times of crisis before I finally shared it with Louise about four years ago.

Opening my scrapbook on the table, I felt that I was opening the door once again to exposing my naked self and re-manifesting my darkest silent shadows. However, despite my immense vulnerability, I felt a sense of safety with Louise. I knew nothing of what those shadows held, other than their language of anxiety, as they raised their familiar voices towards a crescendo in the deepest depths of my being once again.

At first, Louise and I briefly talked about whether this was a picture that I had drawn myself or whether it had possibly been drawn by my brother. (There were other pictures in my scrapbook that had clearly been drawn by an older child.) While I have no memory of drawing the picture myself, I did speak to my brother at a later stage. He told me that he did not think he had drawn the picture and that it did not evoke a strong emotional response in him as it did for me. All I was certain of was the immediate impact that the picture had on me emotionally when I first discovered it, and how it had haunted me for many years since then. It seemed to be screaming two things at me simultaneously: "Close this scrapbook now" and "You will need to re-open it in the future onto this same page."

As Louise and I explored the picture, my anxiety was contained to some extent until I tried to put into words what followed on from the arrow after the figures of Jesus and the Law. Suddenly, my anxiety was transformed into tears as I tried to say that there appeared to be something coming out from between the man's legs towards the face of the smaller figure. The words got stuck in my throat and somehow felt as if they were becoming disconnected from each other, struggling to string themselves together to form a coherent sentence. My anxiety was finally released as tears flowed for a very short, yet intense moment. I felt like an unborn baby bird pecking at the seemingly impenetrable eggshell surrounding me, before finally struggling to hatch from the comfortable safety of my shell, as the words I was choking on were released. I wanted to fly back into the safety of my shell, but my wings had been badly broken in the process of hatching. I now had no choice but to begin the journey of learning to fly, with Louise as the wind beneath my broken wings.

After managing to move through the tears and beginning to further explore the picture, I felt completely lost in my search for an answer to Louise's next question, "Who is missing in this picture?" I was lost in the battlefield of my mind, once again confined by the boundaries that had contained my emotional safety and almost defined my sanity for most of my life. As I mentally identified each character in the picture, my mind remained completely blank as to the answer I was searching for. At the same time, it felt as if my heart was floating in an invisible, distant emotional vacuum somewhere in outer space. My soul seemed to have remained almost completely detached. Suddenly, the long silence was broken when Louise posed the possible answer to the question with the words "parents" or "mother and father". I spontaneously erupted into a volcanic explosion of lava tears pouring down my face, burning into the very core of my being a large, yet invisible hole where, just as quickly, they seemed to disappear and re-solidify. The lava flow stopped abruptly as the volcano subsided, but its burn marks were deeply and permanently engraved in my heart.

I now understand that my spontaneous response of intense grief to the realisation that my parents were absent in this picture must have been significant. They certainly must have been unavailable to me as much-needed support when this happened to me.

As we came to the end of the therapy session, I was left with knowing one thing with certainty – this was to remain an active volcano for many years to come. What I did not know, however, was how the cracks now appearing in the underground movement of tectonic plates in my unconscious would shift my centre of gravity back towards re-connecting with my soul. I knew not how my raw lava tears would solidify into the most beautiful crystals whose beauty was formed through their original state of brokenness.

7

CRAZINESS

Hazel

Figure 2
The view from my back garden

I have been plagued with fluctuating levels of self-doubt over the last twenty-five years or more; ever since I first allowed the question, "Have I been sexually abused?" to enter my awareness. Initially, in this chapter, I want to share with you my journey before meeting Louise; my battle with this unanswered question of whether or not I had been sexually abused, and its resulting sense of "craziness" for me. The final resolution to this followed soon after I started therapy with Louise.

My first clear recollection of my answer to this question goes back to a psychologist's room when I was a young student in my early twenties. "Don't put ideas into my head" (or something similar) was my response when we explored the possibility that I had been sexually abused. Ironically, my mother's response more recently was almost exactly that: "Did that psychologist that you saw when you were a student infect your mind with this idea?"

While seeing this psychologist as a young student, I wrote a letter to a family member. In the letter, I asked a range of questions regarding our upbringing, including the question of whether or not they were aware of me ever having been sexually abused. I got no response to the letter at all from this family member, but I did receive some criticism from other members of my family for having accused this person of having sexually abused me. This plunged me into further self-doubt that felt as if it could destroy my sense of sanity. For many years, I put this sense of "craziness" away somewhere safely on a shelf, only for it to be dislodged again about ten years later when I found a letter that this person had written in response to my letter, but had never posted to me. It answered all the other questions I had asked, and included a brief, factual answer denying any knowledge of me ever having been sexually abused. Why had the letter been kept all that time? My craziness returned and slowly started to eat away at the very core of my soul. Over time, it became more difficult for me to re-shelve my "craziness" in a vacuum-sealed package on the shelf. The sealant began to wear thin as more experiences began to seep through.

While having therapy sessions with the first psychologist mentioned above, as a young student, I acquired a little teddy bear from a friend and took it with me everywhere I went. She initially became my link to my foster mother, and I experienced tremendous anxiety when separated from this bear. Retrospectively, I realised that this teddy bear had become what's called a "transitional object" (Winnicott, 1953) in developmental psychology. It represented all the mothering and love that I had received from my foster mother, enabling me to have a fantasised bond with her once again. At some stage, I felt an immensely strong urge to cover up the bear's body all the time, and it caused me tremendous anxiety to see her naked. In my moments of solitude, I felt the need for a release from this anxiety, and so I spontaneously started to do some creative writing around the theme of "My little body". I was overwhelmed with an intense sense of grief from an unknown source when reading it afterwards. It was around this time that I experienced dissociative dreams with specific sexual content.

Perhaps some of the most intense experiences were those I had at a Holotropic Breathwork workshop I attended as part of my Psychology Honours course. There I expressed myself mostly through drawing after a breathwork experience that spoke to me primarily through some type of trauma in my sexual body. At this workshop, I also experienced immense terror in response to a cobra snake that I sculpted from clay. I knew I had to pass through this snake, but I was overwhelmed with terror and anxiety. I could not look directly at it or touch it. (See Figures 3 and 4.)

Figure 3
Replica snake clay model

(Note: This clay sculpture is a replica of the original one. In the process of re-creating it about 25 years later, I realised that this same snake held no power over me anymore – it could not even raise its head without being supported by the glass standing behind it. With this realisation, my tears started to flow as they dissolved away my fears with an intense sense of relief.)

Figure 4
Snake drawing at Holotropic Breathwork workshop

After the workshop ended, I was so emotionally broken and overwhelmed that I was unable to return to university with the other students, and I stayed behind for a few days. I felt traumatised and was unable to finish my course that year. I nearly lost my Psychology Honours degree after a great financial struggle, but I managed to complete it on a part-time basis over two years, as I tried to pick up the pieces. That year of my life marked the beginning of my healing from sexual abuse, as well as the beginning of my personal empowerment gained from finally breaking free from financial dependence on my parents.

After completing my degree and moving to England for twelve years, my life shifted mostly towards the here-and-now, making a new life for myself overseas and moving through many different jobs and places of accommodation. However, the skeletons in my cupboard re-incarnated when I married my first husband without really exploring our sexuality together before we got married, and in spite of knowing that he was bisexual. Our marriage ended in divorce three years later when I realised that we could not reignite our sexual life. Our sexual life could perhaps best be described as "functional" from the start. I somehow felt that I was "going through the motions" and never experienced an orgasm while making love with him. I could have been trying to follow instructions from a book! However, I had never known anything else, so I never really knew what was missing. I experienced a crisis when I realised that I no longer wanted to be in a platonic marriage with my best friend. I had lost (or had I never found?) my sexuality as a woman, but I knew that I wasn't ready to let it die completely. With this realisation came a huge emotional crisis, as my sexuality still wanted to be born but was scared to come out of hiding in the darkness of shame.

For the next four years, I remained in a relative "comfort zone" of being free and single, relatively disconnected from my sexuality again, and in a job that was "safe and secure" although not personally fulfilling. When I finally resigned from my job, I was thrown into a major crisis of deep depression, which confronted me with the mess that my life was in – both personally (I no longer wanted to be single) and professionally (I had completely lost my sense of direction, knowing I did not want to return to my previous teaching post, but having no sense of which new direction I wanted to take). After an immensely difficult year of mid-life crisis, I met my second husband shortly after finding work as a teaching assistant and part-time teacher at a local school. I loved the work. A new chapter in my life was about to begin as I finally started to awaken to a newfound sense of my sexuality with my second husband. There was sexual fire and passion between us, and I finally experienced orgasm while making love; I was finally re-awakening as a sexual woman at the ripe age of about thirty-six!

We moved to South Africa together from England, shortly after marrying. Despite financial and circumstantial stress, our hearts and souls were happy with our new lifestyle on a farm in sunny South Africa. Once again, I landed myself in a "comfort zone" in an unfulfilling job as a receptionist at a local guest farm.

It was shortly before I scaled down to a part-time position on this job, planning to leave, that my soul-searching led me back to doing a diploma course in counselling. This was not long before I met Louise. It was at this stage that I felt the need to try to discover the source of my "craziness" and to try and find closure with it so that I could move towards being a good therapist myself. Once again, I entered another psychologist's office.

One memory that remains deeply engraved on my soul is of a session in which my therapist was attempting to decrease my overwhelming anxiety by getting me to use deep relaxation techniques while imagining a screen in front of me with an image of what was causing my fear. I was told to imagine that I held the remote control for the image on the screen, and that only when he touched me gently on my hand would the image be able to come to life – until then, the movie was still on pause. I felt deeply relaxed but was suddenly thrown into cold terror and hysteria as I screamed out loudly. I became completely engulfed by fear but had no mental association with the source of my fear at all. Afterwards, the psychologist told me that it was immediately after he had touched my hand that I had screamed. I recovered quickly and grounded myself with his help, despite the intensity of my fear. Unfortunately, I was not able to continue seeing him, as we adopted our son, Joshua, soon after that first session. Little did I know at the time that Joshua would be the one to take me back towards facing that terror.

My sense of "craziness" visited me again shortly after we adopted Joshua. There was an occasion during which I responded totally inappropriately to my husband who was drying Joshua after his bath – I implied that he was touching him in a sexually inappropriate manner. This caused a lot of strain between my husband and me, and it ended in a flood of tears as he encouraged me to start attending therapy with Louise. During that time, my dreams also started to return to an old theme from the past – although I can't recall having any night terrors as such at the time, there were more symbolic dreams that spoke to me of deep shame concerning my body.

I vividly recall a later incident that occurred when Joshua was a toddler and playfully pulled on my trouser pants from behind me as I was leaning down to get something out of the kitchen cupboard. He caught me completely unaware as my world briefly turned into a blurred, slow-motion movie picture in which I initially felt immense, uncontrolled rage of such intensity that I was truly frightened that I would lash out and hurt Joshua. This was quickly followed by a sense of sudden overwhelming grief and sadness as tears welled up in my eyes, springing with immense pressure through the cracks from an underground well deeply hidden. Just as quickly as my tears subsided, they were followed by a strong sense of spiritual peace, stillness and calm in which I knew that I was going to be all right and had control of myself again. Although my emotions did not have any specific mental associations or memories linked to them, they were so intense that it still feels like yesterday as I write about it now. While I was emotionally shaken by this experience due to its intensity, I was also somewhat relieved at how, being alone, I managed to contain my emotions at the time and to continue taking care of Joshua. In sharing this experience with Louise, I realised retro-spectively that, despite its intensity, something had still enabled me to become centred and grounded again relatively quickly. Having been brought up as a Spiritualist, I had always believed that I had a guardian angel and I now realised that she must have been my source of strength. However, while I felt some sense of relief in realising that my experience of the incident with Joshua must have been some kind of flashback, I still felt overshadowed by a sense of "craziness", as I had no specific associated memory of being sexually abused.

If you are a survivor of sexual abuse and recall
similar experiences when your body reacted with
deep shame, then our
"6 Steps To Trusting Your Body" free gift
is exactly what you need. You can find it at
www.TooCloseToRemember.com

While my self-doubt continued, on a mental level, to feed
my thoughts about being "crazy", I think I began to emotionally
disengage from this feeling of "craziness". This shift was so subtle
that I am only aware of it now while writing and reflecting on it.
It finally found a sense of completion quite unexpectedly during
a session with Louise that we had at my house. This session
remains very clear in my memory and it marked a significant
turning-point in my healing journey – one from which there
would be no return …

After a training session, Louise offered to take me home. We
drove together from town and upon arriving at my house, I realised that I had left my front door keys behind. Louise decided to
stay with me, until my husband came home. She and I managed
to get through the garden gate and sat down in the back garden
overlooking the mountains that surrounded us. As a welcome
change, I felt quite relaxed at the beginning of our chat. I started
to reflect on all the different languages spoken by my unconscious
in its attempt to express itself over the previous twenty years or
so – the symbolic language of my dreams, the mental language
of my thoughts, the emotional language of my heart and, most
significantly, the physical language of my body. Initially, I once
again found myself in the middle of a battle between the two
enemies of my mind and my soul. I had no conscious memory
associated with any of these experiences, so I could not trust
what they seemed to be trying to tell me. The battle raged on in

me as I tried to express it in words, constantly shifting between these two rivals.

Slowly, as I continued to recall more and more, I felt a subtle shift in my need to interpret these different languages – a shift away from my thoughts towards a space a little distance from them; a space where I could disengage from them to some extent. I was no longer directly in battle with my thoughts and, somehow, I knew that I did not need to rely on the tools that I had used for so many years to interpret these different languages – the tools of my mind. These tools always brought me to the same conclusion – without a conscious memory, I could never know with absolute certainty what had happened to me and I could never find peace with what I did not know.

Then Louise reflected to me that there was a part of me that knew that I had been sexually abused, but that my mind kept refusing to accept this because I had no memory. Suddenly, it was as if a huge weight had been lifted from me when I told Louise that I knew that this had happened to me and that I had been sexually abused. I felt a deep sense of peace that I had never really experienced before – my battle had been overcome. I was finally trusting my soul and, although I couldn't quite define it, there was a sense that I was beginning a new phase of my healing journey.

When Louise asked me whether I felt it was necessary for me to retrieve an autobiographical conscious memory of specifically what had happened in order to find emotional closure, I knew that my journey did not need to follow that path. Louise then moved onto asking me what it was that I did need to know in order to heal. In my reply to her lay the answer to the next chapter of my healing – I needed to know who had done this to me. However, the answer seemed like an Everest that I would never be able to summit – I feared that I would remain where I was at the base camp, and I could see no path ahead beyond that point.

As I reflected on the session, my knowledge of repression, which I had gained as a psychology student, started to come to life as a lived experience. (Repression is the blocking of an experience out of conscious awareness at a subconscious level so that you have no memory of it.) I now truly understood why I had no memory of the sexual abuse – it was simply too traumatic to remember; and my not being able to remember anything did not mean that it did not happen. I knew the theory but, until then, I had not been able to apply it to my own life. My world was somehow moving in slow motion again, but this time it was a slow motion in which I felt a sense of inner harmony with which I could synchronise myself, despite feeling somewhat disengaged from the world around me. At the same time, I experienced a sense of the immediate space around me expanding. In some way it was creating a place for the musical language of my soul to extend its boundaries beyond the language of my thoughts – the self-doubt that had almost come to define my sense of self for so many years. A children's song that I had had on cassette tape as a student flowed through me, starting with the words, "Peace be with you, in every moment ... let the spirit shine upon you ...". I slowly started to see myself from a new perspective – I was not crazy anymore; I was a survivor of sexual abuse.

8

OUR SOUL KNOWS

Louise

Our soul knows. I'll say it again: we know. We really do know an incredible amount about deep, complex concepts. There are so many things that we do know, but that we don't allow into our awareness. The problem is *not* that we don't know, because we do know. The problem comes in that, for whatever reason, it is hard to acknowledge the truth or the knowing. The reason most often is that we don't want to "deal" with the problem or solution; it is too unsettling or doesn't fit within our preconceived ideas or rules or beliefs. The truth is too hard to swallow, and our defence mechanisms kick in. We intellectualise or rationalise the problem, or even deny what we know.

Perhaps the truth will require that we give up a belief we have; a belief we are convinced serves us well or is core to who we are. For example, we may know that we should leave a job that is killing our soul, but we believe that a stable income is necessary for us to have a "good life" or to be a "good provider". We may believe that we need to maintain a certain standard of living or a certain position in society or in our circle of friends or family. This may cause us to ignore the promptings we receive from our

57

soul. Alternatively, we may keep ourselves so distracted with technology, music, movies, etc., that we never tune into our soul.

As I briefly mentioned previously, collectively (or what was previously referred to in psychological terminology as "unconsciously"), we are aware of covert dynamics or tensions even if we are not able to consciously explain them. In Jungian terms, this is referred to as the "collective unconscious", and in psychodrama terms it is referred to as the "tele" or the wisdom of the group. However, I do not think that it is confined to a group setting. First impressions are an example of our souls knowing. When you meet someone for the first time, you are still able to accurately and intuitively "know" things about the person, even though you have never seen each other before and you have not said a word to each other. You know intuitively, but then your mind kicks in and starts providing mind-chatter that brings specific past experiences or your ego into the picture. This can change the way you would have approached the person if you had just listened to your soul. Nietzsche said, "the very first time you meet someone you know all about him and from that point on, you gradually erase these correct impressions."

Do you remember the example of the correct person selected in the group to say the right thing at the right time? How did the person know? Was it just luck? Or was it a coincidence? No, the accuracy and profound depth of the feedback is enveloped with wisdom and sacredness that dispute the notion of coincidence. There is a famous saying of Albert Einstein: "Coincidence is God's way of remaining anonymous" and so you may have heard people refer to coincidences as "God-incidences".

So, we do know things long before they consciously enter our minds. I remember when, not too long ago, I "out-of-the-blue" (coincidentally) sent a friend of mine a YouTube video clip about "marital affairs". The person phoned me and asked what had prompted me to send the video. At the time I couldn't really answer the question. My logic kicked in and I explained it from my mind-chatter perspective, something along the lines of "interesting facts". Three months later, the truth came out that my friend was having an affair at the time I sent the video. When the truth was revealed, I realised that intuitively, on a soul level, I had known. I just couldn't allow the truth to become conscious.

Another example occurred when I was working at Weskoppies Hospital's Adolescent Unit. In an exercise using a projective technique during a therapy session, an adolescent girl told a "fictitious" story about a father burning his family's home. A couple of days later, the news came to the team that her father did indeed set their home alight, shortly after she told the story. She knew.

There is a simple, powerful exercise we use that often surprises people, in that it helps them to connect to divine wisdom and obtain answers to their most pressing questions. If you would like to try it, it requires that you become calm, ground yourself and focus on your breathing. Feel yourself dropping into your True Self and letting go of your ego or false self. This helps to quieten the mind and bypass defences. Now place your hand on your heart. With sincerity, tell your soul that you really want to know the answer. Stating your intention is important. Be aware of the physical/visceral response from your body. Some people say that they want to know, but as soon as they state their intention, they feel their body responding negatively by either increasing the heartbeat or rate of breathing, or by feeling increased tension in the face. You cannot lie to your soul. If you are not sincere about wanting an answer, you will find that no answer will come when you ask. If, however, you are sincere, you can ask your soul any question and an answer will be forthcoming. The answer can come in the form of a song's lyrics or tune (as in Hazel's case), or in the form of an image or a voice talking inside yourself. Sometimes, the answer will come to you after a few days, when your apprehension around the answer is "forgotten". The questions can be as simple as "Should I go on a vacation to France?" or

"Should I leave my current job or career?", where only a "Yes" or "No" answer is required. However, even more complex questions can be asked, such as "What should I be doing with my life?" or "What is the next step I should take?"

To help you experience this powerful
"Hand-On-The-Heart" technique, we have included
a free guide detailing the exercise
step-by-step at
www.TooCloseToRemember.com
so you can be guided by your soul.

As you read Hazel's story, be aware of how often the answers come to the fore. First of all, notice that each time, the mind is informed to take a back seat. This is important, because if a person stays in the mind, logic will colour and filter the insights/wisdom of the soul. Secondly, notice that Hazel is guided to her True Self, where the ego will be bypassed, so that she can connect with her soul. Lastly, notice that the soul is provided with a manner of communication, whether it is writing, drawing, painting or moving. The actual method, i.e. painting or drawing or writing, is not so important.

What is interesting in Hazel's journey is that Hazel knew all along that she had been sexually abused. It is a fact that infiltrated her whole life and resulted in various outcomes: the selection a homosexual first husband; disturbing sexual dreams that shook her to her core and woke her up sweating and screaming; increased visceral messages from her body when seeing the picture she had drawn as a child and in response to sexual experiences; dissociations from her body; and exaggerated responses when her son jokingly pulled her pants. Yet, despite all of this evidence, she doubted herself because she had no living memory. If you read material on kinesiology, you will notice that they use techniques where the body answers questions, as our bodies are so closely linked to our souls. Similarly, not only Hazel's soul but also her body was screaming to her, for more than twenty years, the message that she had been sexually abused. When she tried to have hypnotherapy to see if she could recall a memory, she responded with outright hysteria when the therapist just touched her hand – a reaction far too severe for a normal stimulus.

What can be asked is, "Why doesn't she have a memory?" Part of the answer will be revealed a little later in Hazel's journey. At this stage, suffice to say that I believe the amnesia was serving as a protective mechanism for her psyche. Interestingly, "psyche" is the Latin word for "soul".

Another question that could be asked is, "Why did Hazel not respond to all these messages from her soul?" I think this is an excellent example of how the mind can be dead set on a specific belief and not tolerate an alternative way of thinking or believing. Hazel was not living her life; she was going through the motions, day after day, because so much of her psychic energy was being used to suppress the idea of having been sexually abused. When energy is used for one task, it means that the energy has been taken from another area of life, as energy cannot be created or destroyed but only transferred or transformed. Clearly her energy was trapped, and she was merely existing. Her life was a constant struggle. She was not thriving or even living; she was focused on surviving, one day to the next.

I vividly recall the afternoon when Hazel could finally admit to herself that she had been sexually abused. We were at her home but were locked out and sat on the stoep (veranda) overlooking their back garden. As Hazel spoke, it became obvious that she was speaking a deep truth about being sexually abused. As soon as she voiced the certainty of it, her mind would kick in and she would logically explain in detail why this could not be true. However, while she "logically" disputed it, her anxiety levels increased, her body "screaming" the incongruence of her logic. This pattern of "Yes, I have been abused, I know it" followed by "No, it's not possible I've been abused, I don't have a memory" continued for most of the session, with Hazel vacillating between a quiet, strong truth of knowing and a chaotic, anxious-filled denial, walking up and down as she was having this "argument" with herself. At one point in the session, I was struck by the increasing difference between the two poles. Looking at Hazel, I said, "But Hazel, you do know the truth. Your body and soul already know the answer, even if your mind is kicking against it." That is all I said. I didn't add anything else. She stopped talking. She looked at me and said, "Yes, you are right. I know I have been sexually abused. I have known for a long time. But how will others believe me if I don't have a memory?" The most notable feature of the statement she made was the deep serenity that accompanied and followed it. She breathed. Her shoulders dropped. She sat down. She was at rest. We decided for the moment not to worry about what others would believe or not believe, or who the abuser was, or what she remembered. Until the end of the session, we just sat together, acknowledging the truth Hazel had known for a long time and had found the courage, for the first time, to acknowledge to herself and to me: "I have been sexually abused". Within minutes, Hazel's general anxiety levels decreased, and her facial expression changed. It was as if a veil had been lifted from her eyes. I have experienced on numerous occasions that, as my clients progress in therapy, they become more beautiful, because they become more themselves – their True Selves. That is what started to happen to Hazel that afternoon. Much water was still to pass under the bridge, but Hazel never again, in our journey, questioned whether she had been sexually abused. She knew – her soul and body knew. And from what transpired in that session, I knew too.

From this point in Hazel's journey, we can see how denying our soul's wisdom, our connection to God, often leads us down long and difficult paths. At times, our mind or ego will kick against our soul's wisdom, convincing us that it is not possible, or that it is too difficult. However, the truth is that denying our soul's wisdom is even more destructive to our True Self.

READER'S REFLECTION

Do you have a truth that you know and are not acknowledging in your life currently? Or do you need to make an important decision? Trust that your soul knows the answer. No matter how frightening the answer may seem, for now you don't need to do anything about it or even have insight into how the answer will come to pass. All we want to do for now, is just to acknowledge that you know the truth, and to voice your truth out loud; to nobody in particular but yourself. While you say it aloud, be aware of your body's response. The True Self and your soul are a place of peace, while the false self or ego will be filled with anxiety as logic and mind-chatter kick in. As you verbalise aloud, notice whether a sense of relief fills you – a relief in giving the truth a voice.

9

FIRST ST. RAPHAEL'S SANCTUARY
HEALING RETREAT – JULY 2015

Hazel

Approximately six months after making peace with the realisation that I had most definitely been sexually abused, I attended Louise's St Raphael's Sanctuary Healing Retreat. It was my first experience of a healing retreat of this nature. I recall being both exhausted and excited when Louise invited me to attend, as I needed a break and some "time out" to recharge myself. While I was to some extent aware of my own "skeletons" that I had to deal with, I could never have comprehended at the time the challenges that lay ahead for me at the retreat.

I will write here about the three main therapeutic experiences I had during this first retreat – my experience of painting, followed by the left- and right-handed journaling technique, and finally the second letter of forgiveness, which followed on from my experience of immense rage.

PAINTING:

Figure 5
"Mess" – Painting at first St. Raphael's Retreat

At first, I stared at the blank sheet of cardboard in front of me, surrounded by bottles of paint, paintbrushes and a silence that loudly rattled around in my head with an ever-increasing volume of repetitive thoughts like, "Which paintbrush should I use and which colours? What shall I paint?" followed by, "I am useless at painting. I don't have an ounce of artistic ability in me." As I peered over at the other people whose paintings were starting to take shape, the volume only became more deafening. I felt like a radio stuck on one channel, continually rewinding and replaying the same track. I felt immobilised and unable to change the channel I was on, because I *was* the radio; I was not just listening to the radio. I sat alone for what seemed like an eternity, my noisy head and silent heart consuming my whole being, still with a blank sheet of cardboard in front of me.

Gradually, I allowed myself to recall Louise's words of guidance just before starting the painting activity: "Try not to think too much or have any preconceived ideas about what you are going to paint. Just pick up a paintbrush and start painting." Her words whispered softly to me. Once again, my head attempted to betray my soul with the questions, "Did I hear her correctly? Is this really so simple? It can't be, surely?"

Despite the battle between my head and soul, I picked up the closest paintbrush, slowly moved it towards a pot of red paint and started painting by placing the paintbrush onto the cardboard, moving it around with no sense of direction or form, repetitively using the same colour. Slowly, each stroke of my paintbrush seemed to facilitate my ability to find a part of myself that could listen to the radio and somehow separate myself from it, despite the noise it continued to create. Although my hands slowly started to flow with the paintbrush between the paint pots and the cardboard, I was still aware that I was unable to change the channel on the radio that I was then able to listen to. However, as I listened to the radio, my hands continued to flow more spontaneously with the paintbrush as I became more relaxed.

Very slowly, I began to feel a deeper sense of inner peace and calm as my paintbrush created the different colours and forms emerging on my cardboard. Gradually, it seemed as if my hands intuitively knew what to do as they tuned into my soul channel. Looking back now, I realise that it was the simple physical process of picking up the paintbrush and starting to paint that allowed me to change channels on the radio. Without being aware of it at the time, a new view into my unconscious was being opened through the painting process, without an ounce of artistic ability in me. Once I had finished the painting, I felt quite disturbed when I looked at it, but my anxiety levels had significantly decreased and I experienced something shifting in me, although I could not define exactly what it was.

LEFT- AND RIGHT-HANDED JOURNALING TECHNIQUE:

After we had finished painting, we were instructed to write a series of questions and answers using different colours and different hands. A question was written in one colour using the dominant hand. Then the answer was written in a different colour using the non-dominant hand. The questions and answers I wrote during the activity related to the picture I had painted. (See Figure 5.) They are represented here below.

Q: **What are you trying to tell me?**
A: I have a block

Q: **I have a block about what?**
A: I have a block about something violent, something dark, something closed, something that wants to find some light. For God's sake just let it be free. There is white and light on the other side. Who the fuck has created this mess?

Q: **What is the blue and purple?**
A: Wisdom, healing

Q: **What is the red and black?**
A: Violence, aggression

There are two memories of this painting/writing activity that are very vivid to me. The first thing I remember is the sense of having a complete block as to what the painting was trying to tell me. When looking at the first question, the answer presented nothing but a blank screen in front of me – a screen that, no matter how long I stared at it, remained blank. I had absolutely no idea what to write. The second thing I remember is that, as I wrote the next question that Louise prompted to me ("I have a block about what?"), my mind initially remained blank until I picked up the pen and started writing the beginning of the answer, "I have a block about ...", using my left hand. Quite unexpectedly, my pen started writing and moving along the page with a life of its own, no longer needing my mind to tell it what to write. As my pen flowed along the page, I felt a sense of peaceful detachment while a part of me calmly watched what

I was writing. Louise came around and, after glancing over my writing, asked me whether I was dissociating. I replied that I was alright and that I was not dissociating. In fact, despite the disturbing content of what I was writing, I felt a deep sense of inner peace enfolding me as the words appeared on the page in front of me. As with my experience of painting, it was the experience of picking up the pen and writing again that started to release my mental block.

My anxiety levels slowly increased as each group member took a turn to share their experience with the group and receive feedback from the group. I perceived in everyone's painting some level of realism; something recognisable that could be explained or interpreted and linked to their life experience, and that could be shared with the group on a level at which they felt comfortable. All their paintings seemed to be light or at least contain some movement from dark towards light. There didn't seem to be one painting that was completely abstract in its appearance, like mine. I was struggling to actively engage with the group as I became lost in my own world, and waves of anxiety and self-doubt washed over me. My thoughts rolled around in my head while I wondered how I could share this dark, totally abstract mess with anyone in the group when I didn't yet fully understand what it was about. My turn came and I chose to share some of my fears with the group. When I shared my painting with the group, I felt a huge sense of relief. A greater sense of relief washed over me as I further shared that there was something wanting to be set free from the two "jails" in my painting. There was, in fact, a light at the centre of the second "jail"– a light that would open the jail and set me free. While my anxiety levels had decreased somewhat at that point, they seemed to be constantly threatening to return, to throw me back into the painted mess in front of me.

FORGIVENESS LETTER 1: RAGE

For this activity, I was instructed to write a letter to someone who had hurt me and whom I struggled to forgive. I needed to

68

express my feelings of hurt and anger without any censorship, explaining the impact of their hurt in my life. The transcript of what I wrote is presented below.

> Because of what you have done I have lived with disliking myself as a woman for so long, lost my first marriage due to this exact issue, spent loads of money on counselling, had no confidence in myself, my body, my intuition until now. Now I have had to struggle with not knowing who you are – the struggle is never ending – YOU CAN DIE AND ROT IN YOUR GRAVE KNOWING THAT YOU HAVE DONE THIS AND THAT I KNOW. I will do more than just survive – DESPITE YOU – YOU FUCKING BASTARD – JUST STAY AWAY FROM ME FOREVER AND LIVE IN YOUR BIG BUBBLE OF DENIAL – You don't deserve to live any-more – But I WILL MOVE FORWARDS.

While I cannot recall much of my experience of writing this letter, my most vivid memory is of me sitting alone in the workshop venue (after lunch) after having written this letter. I was really frightened of damaging some of Louise's personal possessions in the room. I felt as if I was an exploding fuse box; completely out of control and about to pick up anything within reach to smash it to pieces until it wouldn't shatter anymore. As I look back on it now, I am sure that my guardian angel must have been close to me as, fortunately for Louise, I managed not to act on my raging impulses.

FORGIVENESS LETTER 2: UNDERSTANDING AND COMPASSION

By the time we were instructed to write a second letter on the retreat, I had become so emotionally overwhelmed with rage, and fragile with anxiety, that I felt unable to write the letter we had been instructed to write. (We had been instructed to write another letter to the same person, but from a more open heart-space in which to attempt to find some compassion for them, by trying to understand why they had hurt us.) Instead, I chose to write a different letter. If I recall correctly, I wrote a letter of thanks to my foster mother. However, by that stage my mind, body and soul had reached a saturation point and I fell sick with the flu. I slept through most of the rest of the retreat.

Having opened up this well of pain, but having terminated the group process early, I went to see Louise individually a while after the retreat, to try to explore this issue further and to find closure. It was then that I wrote the second letter, presented below.

Dear _____

So why did you do this to me?? You felt powerless as a husband, as a man, as someone who is meant to be strong, you never knew love from your own father, you had no sense of self, no sense of who you are, dependent, useless and sexually unfulfilled – that does NOT give you an excuse AT ALL – just helps me to understand why you did what you did to me (and) you have to try and prove your power by abusing me? Did it make you feel more powerful again?? YOU ARE NOT EXCUSED AND YOU HAVE NOT DESTROYED ME. I really don't know if I can find any compassion for you, perhaps just understanding somehow. You took the easy, spineless route to deal with your problems – you took them out on me – you had no (strength) to face yourself. (The) abused becomes the abuser – is that what happened to you – YOU CHOSE NOT TO FACE UP TO YOURSELF – instead you ran away – TO ME – MADE YOUR PROBLEMS MY PROBLEM – YOU SPINELESS FOOL. YOU WILL NEVER FACE UP TO THIS – DENIAL IS EASIER – I AM STRONGER THAN YOU AND ALWAYS HAVE BEEN – I FACE MYSELF – what do I see??

Pain, abuse, tears, loss – all of these were where you came from, what you hid away from, what you could not face –

70

I look in the mirror – I face my pain, unlike you.

Am I your daughter?

I have struggled immensely to recall my personal emotional experience of writing this letter. As I read through the transcript, I realised the immense significance of it and felt frustrated that my memory of writing it was so unclear. While I struggled to place the pieces of my memory into the larger puzzle of my healing journey, I realised that the emotion that I had experienced at the time of writing did not necessarily reflect the emotional content of the words written. I finally concluded that the reason why I could not clearly recall my emotional experience of writing this letter is that due its highly emotive content, I was searching for a memory of high emotional intensity. It is possible that that was simply not my experience while writing, despite the content of the letter. It is possible that I was searching with my mind rather than my soul; using binoculars set to the wrong focus lens.

As I gradually began to switch my lenses, I started to recall that my writing had flowed freely throughout most of the letter. I had felt mostly calm but somewhat emotionally disengaged from what I was writing – almost as if it could have been someone else who was writing the letter. At times, it was as if I were watching someone else writing from a little distance away, yet I was not dissociating as such. If I recall correctly, I shifted slightly from this disengaged space towards myself as moments of anger emerged and were then subdued by insightful moments of realizing my inner strength. I was like a wave on the ocean: just as quickly as my anger built up, the wave crashed, allowing its energy to be dispersed back into the calmer depths of the ocean, before the next wave emerged. From a short but relatively safe distance, I seemed to flow with the waves until I felt as if the last wave had crashed. It was finally dispersed on reaching the shoreline – my letter was complete.

I remember when I sat with my completed letter in front of me. At first, I felt that I had moved into a blank space in my mind – a blank space that somehow needed filling, although I could not quite define how. After I had remained in the blank space for a little while, I realised that I had not ended the letter with a name or a statement of whom it was from. Suddenly the words, "Am I your daughter?" dropped from the heavens and I re-entered the violent battlefield of my mind. As my mental battle ensued over whether or not I could write these words on the letter, another blank space emerged briefly. In this blank space, my pen won the battle as it wrote the words at the bottom of the page. I was not really aware at the time that this was the first of many battles to come in the war to be waged.

When I had finished, Louise asked me to read through the letter again and then take another piece of paper and write down any positive affirmations that I could take away with me from this letter. As I did so, the affirmations flowed quite spontaneously onto the page:

I AM STRONGER THAN YOU

I AM STRONGER THAN WHAT YOU HAVE DONE TO ME

I RISE ABOVE YOU.

The only vaguely intense emotional moment I recall was when I read out the second affirmation, "I am stronger than what you have done to me." A deeply raw sadness threatened to explode in me and seemed to be connected to the second part of the sentence: "... what you have done to me." My safe, slightly disengaged distance away from myself suddenly shortened dramatically before I managed to take just one step back as the gap closed in on me.

Looking back, I now realise that the raw grief and pain related to this letter were finally expressed a year later, on the second healing retreat, when I wrote a second version of this same letter. However, there were many more steps on my journey before the second retreat.

10

ST. RAPHAEL'S SANCTUARY HEALING RETREAT: REFLECTIONS ON HAZEL'S FIRST RETREAT

Louise

Our St Raphael's Sanctuary Healing Retreats are designed to bring the two truths of theology and psychology together in a comprehensive way. Having worked in private psychiatric clinics and hospitals, and within my role as occupational therapist, I had been warned by superiors and colleagues not to bring up any spiritual aspects in therapy. However, through my journey I realised that true healing cannot occur if the spiritual aspect is not incorporated into the healing process. Being aware of the contradictions between the medical model and the path of insight I was on, my brother and I set out to develop a healing programme that could incorporate both elements. As Kathleen Singh, a long-time hospice worker, calls it, we were developing a psycho-spiritual programme. We are cognisant that the body is an important element in ensuring intra-connectedness (connection between the mind, body and soul of each person). However, due to time and resource restraints, we had to limit our focus to the psycho-spiritual elements (mind and soul).

While it is not possible to discuss the St Raphael's Sanctuary programme in detail here, (see the resources section at the back of the book), I will provide a brief overview of the approach used at St Raphael's Sanctuary Healing retreats. The goal for the St Raphael's Sanctuary Healing retreat is to guide people with mental and spiritual dis-ease to connect to their soul which is connected to God or Divine wisdom. This connection becomes a conduit that will show them the pathway to their own healing. Each person's path to healing may be different, and that is why it is so important that each person is provided an opportunity to connect to God who will guide their healing. In this way our souls have the potential to lead us to transformation healing if we re-connect and listen to it. The St Raphael's Sanctuary Healing retreat program is designed to dove-tail principles from Jungian psychology with spiritual development and incorporates spiritual perspectives of mental illness. We work faith-based, and weave uniquely developed therapeutic techniques and methods into the healing journey.

In a nutshell, the programme's emphasis is on helping to bring people into contact with their True Self and to work with obstacles that prevent them from living from their soul on a daily basis. As mentioned in the chapter titled "Our Soul Knows," we use a lot of practical sessions, connecting with our True Selves and allowing our souls to guide us through creative sessions to bring us closer to God and others. Amongst others, we assist people in finding their vocation or life purpose, to discern their crosses, to make sense of their suffering, to heal soul-ties and intergenerational bonds, to find hidden treasures in their pain and wounds and if they are ready, to forgive. Our programme runs over eight days so that people can retreat from the world and go inward at their own pace. Our family, also known as the Family of Gentle Healers, presents the healing retreats. We are called to be healers, we are passionate about facilitating people through a healing journey so that people can live an extraordinary life, as God's Beloved.

To return to Hazel's healing journey, the planning phase of our St Raphael's Sanctuary healing retreat programme had been completed and we wanted people to experience the programme and give us feedback so that we could refine the programme. We invited specific therapists who worked in mental health, as well as two priests, as we felt that they could all provide us with valuable feedback on the programme. Knowing Hazel, I invited her to attend as well and to give honest feedback, as she was living the healing journey.

I share some of my memories of Hazel's experiences as I observed them during her first healing retreat that we presented. Within the first four days, it became clear that the experience was overwhelming for her. It was difficult for me to clearly define the reason for it at the time. A number of people who attended the retreat had previously been diagnosed with depression, and so the difference in her experience could not be attributed to the level of mental health; neither could it be clearly attributed to the level of disturbance in her background. Initially I wondered whether the difference was due to her not having been baptised. As Christians, we believe that we are gifted with the Holy Spirit as comforter and guide when we are baptised, as we are given the breath of God that accompanies us throughout our life. The Holy Spirit dwelling in us is constantly trying to move us closer to God; at times subtly nudging us and at other times pushing us. Is it easier to connect with our souls after baptism? Is a question I asked myself and I am still not entirely sure of the answer.

I also wondered whether the difference could be due to the fact that Hazel had not been able to attend our Healing and Deliverance Service at the beginning of the retreat. In this session we deal with soul-ties and intergenerational bonds. She could not stay overnight at the Sanctuary but travelled in and out every day so that she could be home for Joshua, her young son. I had noticed that there had been a noticeable change in the other participants after the service. Somehow, they seemed lighter and the atmosphere at the retreat was tangibly less heavy. There was also more laughter.

My brother has personal experience of parishioners whose lives have changed incredibly after a Healing and Deliverance service. Examples of these changes include stopping substance abuse; reconciling what seemed to be irreparable relationships; finding jobs; and having family members return to spiritual practices. Part of the Healing and Deliverance Service entails letting go of things that can hold us back. I think we often underestimate the power of reconnecting with God, our Creator. St Augustine wrote, "You have made us for yourself, O Lord, and our hearts are restless until they rest in you." There are no words to describe our coming home to God, our Father.

By the time of the first retreat experience, Hazel had already acknowledged that she had been sexually abused, but she was still reluctant to verbalise it aloud to others. When there was an opportunity to share within pairs or in the group setting during the retreat, her communication tended to be vague and ambiguous. One of the first creative sessions of the retreat is spent on connecting to our True Self (soul) and then painting from a soul-space whatever is brought up. The session is completed with an exercise in right-and left-handed journaling. As Hazel sat in front of her poster, I could see her anxiety levels increase. I encouraged her not to think, but to relax, take any colour that "jumped out" at her, and intuitively make any movement or mark that wanted to be painted. Painting can be a daunting task initially, as we have so many ideas about the acceptable ways or things to paint, and we judge ourselves and our painting, all from our false self. However, anything and everything is acceptable if it comes from a soul space, as our souls are wiser than our minds. Again, Hazel was encouraged to move out of her mind, into her body and into her soul; to be led and guided; and to offer a voice, a means for her soul to speak. Slowly she started painting, initially tentatively – red, black and yellow stripes. Later, she painted with more conviction. Almost three years on, I don't recall the themes that emerged from her right-and left-handed journaling, but I still vividly remember her painting her picture. I remember that she was self-conscious of her painting. I also recall that she was significantly moved by the whole experience, although I found it disturbing. Our souls don't lie. Our souls are not wrong, although the message can be overwhelming. However, the message will never bring more than we can handle at any given time. After all, it knows we are spiritual beings, and nothing can change that.

A couple of days later, we started on the theme of forgiveness in the programme. There is much controversy about forgiving perpetrators of sexual abuse. Please understand that at no point do we condone the act of sexual abuse. We do acknowledge that life is complex and that we cannot begin to understand all its complexities. We live in a broken world with broken people, and one day we will understand God our Father's justice, mercy and love, which at times are marred by our too-small, human mind. I would like to state emphatically that at St Raphael's Sanctuary we believe forgiveness is a divine act, but it is *not* something that is forced, especially if people are not ready to forgive. We do believe that forgiveness releases victims and enables them to move on with their lives. Furthermore, the expression of anger and rage is often a very necessary part of the healing process, enabling true forgiveness. Most times, a paradigm shift is needed for forgiveness to be heartfelt. Once the forgiveness comes from the soul, it is usually transformative in nature and something incredibly beautiful emerges. From experience, I have seen that when people forgive too soon, without having experienced all the emotions attached to the transgression, the effect of forgiveness is not as deep, nor as transformative. In a sense, the unexpressed emotions hold us back somehow.

At the time of the retreat, I realised that Hazel was not in a space of forgiveness. The instruction for her first letter was to focus specifically on anger, to help her to express all the anger she had felt surrounding her sexual abuse. Her instruction was to write a letter to the abuser, in which she expressed all her emotions. During our sessions before the retreat, the identity of her abuser had not been an issue in any way. We were never focused on a witch-hunt to identify the abuser because Hazel didn't have a memory of the abuse. We looked at how the fact of her sexual abuse impacted on her present life. The idea of the exercise was to use the letter to vent all her feelings and to explain to the unknown perpetrator how the violation had influenced her life and impacted upon her relationships. Having given Hazel the instructions, I could see from her body language that this was going to be a difficult task. I afforded her space, to see what she would choose to do and to step in if I thought she was "drowning". Again, she started slowly and then wrote more and more fervently, faster and faster, until she threw the page aside, jumped up and left the room. I allowed her some space to breathe and walk. After the session, I had a brief chat with Hazel, but she was so upset that there was no point in continuing the conversation. She gave me the letter and I scheduled a session for a week after the retreat, so that we could discuss the letter in private. When Hazel returned the next day, she was physically ill with flu symptoms. She climbed into bed and spent the following two days sleeping. In a sense, she escaped what was, at that time, emotionally and spiritually too overwhelming for her to deal with.

A week later, during our private session, we took a closer look at Hazel's letter of anger and she wrote another letter. In her letter writing, for the first time, she wrote "Are you my father?" The possibility of her father being the perpetrator of the sexual abuse was voiced for the first time – a question that caused a mental meltdown. Just talking about the possibility was a slow process that lasted almost six weeks. At the same time, the frequency of her remembered dreams increased. She also started remembering dreams that she had had as a young adult, when she first sought help. The dreams had intense and, at times, disturbing themes of shame, of sex and of her father.

In summary, the emotional and spiritual themes that arose and were conversed with during the first St Raphael's Sanctuary retreat were relevant to Hazel's healing journey, although the experience was intense and overwhelming. In hindsight, I wonder whether it was too much, too soon in her healing journey, as we see her escaping at the end through illness. What was interesting was that she came to the retreat to sleep; she was not avoidant by staying at home. I would like to think that this was due to the acceptance and sense of belonging she experienced in the group; an acceptance of "No matter what, we accept and love you just where you are presently."

A year later, Hazel asked to attend a second St Raphael's Sanctuary Healing Retreat. The difference between the first and second retreat was incredible! It showed how much progress and healing Hazel had achieved. She had moved from being someone who was overwhelmed, anxious, self-focused and unsure to being someone who could share, support, connect with others and stand her ground, one year later. Between the two retreats, however, there was much work that needed to be done.

To be honest with you, the account of this journey would not be complete without a discussion of my own experience at the time of the first retreat. In reflecting on my own process, at that stage of our journey, I started to severely doubt myself, my "theories" and my own capabilities as a therapist. I felt guilty about having brought Hazel to a place where she seemed "worse off" than when she had arrived. My fears became overwhelming, as I questioned myself: "What if this is all wrong? What if I made her ill? Shouldn't I have known better as a therapist? I've given my life to this – what if I'm wrong? Where does all this leave me? After all, Hazel was supposed to come on the healing retreat and find healing; she was supposed to walk away wiser and stronger, and to make a success of her life so that the story could have a perfect, beautiful ending. I wanted to rescue her and fix it all. Instead, she is ill, anxious and overwhelmed. And, to make matters worse, she suddenly suspects her father of sexual abuse. What if she is wrong? What if she is right?"

I questioned my motives: "Am I doing this for myself, for my ego, to prove myself?" It became too much for me. I became anxious and reached a point where I was rendered powerless. I resolved to see Hazel at our next session, to make sure she was "OK under the circumstances", and then to refer her on to someone else. I didn't think I could help her any further. Hazel's crisis had brought me to my own crisis.

READER'S REFLECTION:

At this stage of Hazel's healing journey, and mine, the point of reflection is that there is a time for us to accept our own weaknesses; a time to look our biggest fear in the eye … even just the possibility of it. There is a time to be OK if we don't "get it", if we are flawed, or if we cannot meet our own and others' expectations. There is a time to acknowledge that we fail, we fall, we are imperfect, we become overwhelmed, and life doesn't have perfect people or perfect endings. We can acknowledge it all now and embrace "not being OK".

11

DISSOCIATION

Hazel

Dissociation is defined by the English Oxford Living Dictionary as a "separation of normally related mental processes, resulting in one group functioning independently from the rest". I have experienced dissociation in a variety of forms over the past twenty years and it has left its mark on my life. It has spoken to me in my dreams, as well as in my perceptions of my body (depersonalisation) and my most immediate surroundings (derealisation).

I first experienced dissociation in my dreams. The dreams in which specific sexual content involving unidentified people was revealed were all dreams in which I was in a dissociated state. I was always watching from a safe distance and felt completely emotionally detached, almost as if I was a clinical researcher assessing what I was observing – totally objectively. These dreams revealed the most in terms of what may have happened to me and they left me feeling deeply disturbed and anxious at the time. I recall them as if I had dreamt them yesterday.

More recently, I experienced a sense of being disconnected from my body immediately after unexpectedly seeing my father in a local shop. We exchanged a hello with each other, and I went on my way to work, initially feeling fine. As I was walking along the pavement, I suddenly started to perceive my feet as being somehow detached from my body, as if they were someone else's feet, attached to someone else's body. They were not responding to my brain's instructions to put one foot in front of the other. However, I was not floating completely above and detached from my body as in my dreams – I still experienced being located in my head as I watched these feet that didn't seem to belong to me. My anxiety levels were high, as this experience caught me unawares and I could not associate it with any other familiar experience. My anxiety seemed to feed on itself as I tried to fight it away. When I arrived at work, I called Louise, as I felt caught in a whirlwind of anxiety that was approaching panic. She took me through the process of reconnecting with my senses in my immediate environment, and I performed some breathing exercises until my anxiety subsided and I was able to go on with my work. I soon re-connected with my feet, much to my relief!

Another dissociative experience occurred about an hour after I had a conversation with some people about a young girl who had been removed from her biological parents. She had been sent to the doctor for a physical examination, due to suspected sexual abuse. Again, I felt absolutely fine during the conversation and it was only afterwards, while I was driving home, that I started to disconnect from what was happening around me. As I drove down the farm road on my way home, it was as if I was driving down the road for the first time. I didn't seem to recognise any-one around me, although they were my next-door neighbours. They seemed like total strangers to me; people I had never seen before. While I knew on some level which way to go to get home, again it was as if I was entering the building for the first time – exploring a new house that was a new building, and not my home. At the same time, I seemed to notice more of the finer details of my immediate environment – the tiny cracks in the walls, and the bright orange paint of the cupboards that seemed to shine more brightly, with their dirty marks that were more visible than usual – if there were fingerprints on the cupboards, I would probably have been able to identify whose they were! I experienced a paradoxical sense of increased sensory awareness of the finer details simultaneously with a disconnection from the wider environment around me. I was alone at the time and was too caught up in my own anxiety to recall how to "ground" myself again. After a WhatsApp conversation with Louise, who was about to board a plane, I recalled the grounding techniques and realised that I was able to return to myself again and be my own therapist – out of circumstantial necessity, but thanks to Louise and modern technology!

Finally, and more recently, I again experienced bodily dissociation (disconnecting from my feet as I walked) immediately after finding the free association letter that I had written to my father more than twenty years ago. On this occasion, the experience went away shortly after I talked to my husband about it, but then it recurred at random intervals for a few days after this experience.

When I first experienced dissociation, I did not fully understand what was happening or why it was happening. As a result, my anxiety levels easily escalated towards panic as I re-experienced the feeling of "craziness". I felt as if I was losing all sense of control and contact with reality as my fears escalated. With the passing of time, I have gained confidence and competence in being my own therapist if dissociation decides to pay me a visit – even if the WhatsApp line is unavailable. I have come to be able to interpret the language of dissociation and to understand it as my own means of self-protection. In befriending it rather than fighting it, and by applying some simple grounding techniques that I am now familiar with, I can now manage it more effectively on my own.

READER'S REFLECTION:

You can also learn to manage your own dissociation. The best starting point is to understand that it is trying to be your friend by protecting you from what you perceive to be too overwhelming. Don't do battle with your friend; rather thank it for visiting and then ground yourself by reconnecting with your five senses e.g. breath slowly and deeply, now focus on six sounds you are hearing in your environment; then five objects you can see; four smells in your environment; three textures you are feeling against your skin and become aware of the taste in your mouth. Lastly, take a deep breath and feel yourself relax as you breathe out.

12

THE BROKEN CHILD

Hazel

Louise is an occupational therapist that has specialised in mental health and has more than 30 years' experience in the field. I had already had one session with the psychologist that Louise had referred me to. She felt that in-depth psychoanalysis would help in my healing journey. However, I wanted to continue therapy with Louise, as my therapeutic relationship with her felt right for me, and the logistical problems with transport made it difficult for me to see the psychologist. The closest available psychologist was more than an hour's drive away in a neighbouring town. We chatted about this briefly and agreed that I would continue to see the psychologist once a month or so and see Louise in between these sessions. Shortly after having written the second letter of forgiveness, I became aware that something massive was shifting in me. I felt as if I were a time bomb waiting to explode. For this reason, I decided to try and keep myself as grounded as possible by cycling up to Louise's house for an individual follow-up session, which Louise had offered me after the first St Raphael's Healing Retreat. I recall feeling calm while

I kept rhythm with my breathing on the muddy farm road as I approached her house.

SELECTING AN IMAGE:

During the session, Louise laid out a wide range of picture post-cards and asked me to select the first one that jumped out at me, without allowing myself to think too much.

From the wide range of photo images spread out in front of me, three seemed to jump out at me simultaneously, as if asking me to explore what lay beneath the images. There was a picture of a small porcelain doll with a shattered face; a picture of someone leaping into the air; and a picture of a hand playing a chord on the guitar. (See Figures 6, 7 and 8.)

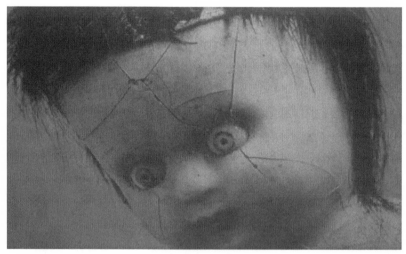

Figure 6
Broken doll postcard

Figure 7
Flying figure postcard

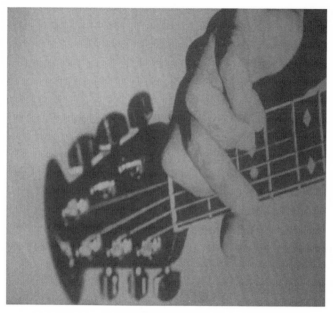

Figure 8
Guitar postcard

Initially, all three of the pictures seemed to be equally important, so I followed Louise's instructions and separated all three of
them from the other pictures. My initial mental struggle in trying
to select just one image to work with seemed to be resolved with
a physical shifting of my hand towards the pictures. It was as if
my hand was being guided towards the two that needed to be
shifted away. I started to become aware that all that I needed to
do was to follow my hand, rather than my thoughts, although
there was still a conflict between the two. Finally, following my
hand's movements, I was left with the photo of the shattered face
of the small porcelain doll.

When asked to identify one word that this picture brought
to mind, I felt as if the word "broken" was spoken to me with
crystal clarity. The voice initially seemed to emerge from a source
beyond myself, and yet at the same time spoke from deep within
myself, in a silence that only I could hear.

WRITING THE LETTER:

Louise then asked me to connect with my wise, inner child and to write a letter from her to my adult self, openly expressing anything important that she wanted my adult self to know. I needed to write spontaneously, without thinking or analysing what I was writing. I also needed to keep my pen moving on the paper all the time, by drawing a figure of eight as many times over as needed when I felt unable to continue writing. The letter I wrote is presented below, together with my reflection on the process.

BROKEN

Dear Hazel

I want you to know that I am OK and that you are doing really well in looking after me now that you are bigger. I am stronger than you realise. I have survived so much and [know] that you are able to heal me without even knowing what's caused me to be broken.

∞

I am wise and I am strong through what I have been through and the more that you allow me to feel [more] than think, the stronger I will become and the more I will be able to heal you, now that you are big.

∞

I need you to trust that I have survived and that I am not weak, my courage is stronger [than] my fear and that the only real fear is fear of fear and fear of feeling me again.

∞

Yes, I was hurt, injured, damaged, abused but my little body survived and you are a beautiful woman. I [want] you to feel that and know [that] it's OK to feel sad when you feel beautiful as a woman.

∞

Yes, I lost my mommy but now [you] are my mommy and Joshua's mommy and you are a wonderful, loving mommy who knows how to love because you had love.

∞

Listen to your big body now and let it heal on its own and with my help, try not to feel ashamed of what it seems to be telling you.

∞

Your big body is strong, it was damaged but it is strong and it has its own language [so] listen to it, and accept it. [It] has its own way of telling you what has happened to me and I want you to know and believe that I am with you, we look after each other and that you also have an angel looking after you – when you fall, I will catch you, and then you will

∞

learn to fly again and help others fly using your strong wings to help them with similar journeys to yours. You don't have to

∞

feel overwhelmed by what has [happened] to me because I know that you will return from this journey stronger than ever.

∞

Follow your songs, your images and try not to think too much.

∞

I will not tell you too much at once but trust what you feel, what you write because this is me speaking to you and I love you and I need you to love me, not feel frightened of me.

∞

Don't think and then hold back.

∞

Your daddy was damaged, so damaged, not even knowing he was. So was your mother but daddy was more damaged.

∞

I want to say goodbye for now, keep cycling. I will send you the people that will help you open your heart to me and what has happened, I have already.

∞

Love me just the way I am.

∞

I will protect you too.

REFLECTIONS ON MY WRITING EXPERIENCE:

Dear Hazel

I want you to know that I am OK and that you are doing really well in looking after me now that you are bigger. I am stronger than you realise. I have survived so much and [know] that you are able to heal me without even knowing what's caused me to be broken.

∞

As soon as my pen hit the paper, it seemed to start moving with its own energy, almost as if my hand, with the pen, was merely a channel for the energy that was moving it. Almost immediately, I experienced a deep sense of inner peace as my pen flowed effortlessly with this unseen energy. The energy flowing through my pen was interrupted when I moved into drawing the figure of eight in the empty space beneath the first set of words, as my thoughts entered onto the scene for the first time and I started to engage in a battle with my mind. However, as the empty space was filled with more figures of eight, the repetitive circular motion of my pen eventually started to quieten my mind. As my eyes started to shift their focus towards the empty space on the page below my pen, it was as if this started to create some space within my thoughts. As the circular motion of my pen continued, thoughtlessness started to shift and make space for new thoughts, finally allowing the pen to move into the empty space below the figures of eight and to flow into writing again.

I am wise and I am strong through what I have been through and the more that you allow me to feel [more] than think, the stronger I will become and the more I will be able to heal you, now that you are big.

∞

I need you to trust that I have survived and that I am not weak, my courage is stronger [than] my fear and that the only real fear is fear of fear and fear of feeling me again.

∞

Yes, I was hurt, injured, damaged, abused but my little body survived and you are a beautiful woman. I [want] you to feel that and know [that] it's OK to feel sad when you feel beautiful as a woman.

∞

Yes, I lost my mommy but now [you] are my mommy and Joshua's mommy and you are a wonderful, loving mommy who knows how to love because you had love.

∞

My pen continued to flow spontaneously like a river. I seemed to become the river, overflowing into a waterfall of tears. The tears obscured my vision, blurring the words I wrote, while the salty liquid started to cleanse my soul. As my spectacles had no windscreen wipers, I had to take them off and I briefly returned to the "here and now" as I heard Louise saying, "Keep going, Hazel." Almost immediately, and quite unexpectedly, I was returned to the grief over the loss of my foster mother. I seemed to have become the Victoria Falls as my tears obscured my writing again. My pen kept moving, while my grief flowed with its movement through the words it created. The synchronisation between my writing and my soul seemed to clear the path ahead. Somehow, I spontaneously allowed my wise inner child to remind me that I was now a mother myself and that I was healing through my love for my son.

> Listen to your big body now and let it heal on its own and with my help, try not to feel ashamed of what it seems to be telling you.

∞

> Your big body is strong, it was damaged but it is strong and it has its own language [so] listen to it, and accept it. [It] has its own way of telling you what has happened to me and I want you to know and believe that I am with you, we look after each other and that you also have an angel looking after you – when you fall, I will catch you, and then you will

∞

> learn to fly again and help others fly using your strong wings to help them with similar journeys to yours. You don't have to

∞

feel overwhelmed by what has [happened] to me because I know that you will return from this journey stronger than ever.

∞

Follow your songs, your images and try not to think too much.

∞

I will not tell you too much at once but trust what you feel, what you write because this is me speaking to you and I love you and I need you to love me, not feel frightened of me.

∞

As my pen flowed back into the repetitive figures of eight, I became still and flowed with it, rather than re-entering a war with my mind. My breathing seemed to follow the circular motion of my pen, with an in-and-out breath following each half figure of eight. My breath and my pen seemed to be moving in harmony as my pen carried my breath through the figures of eight. I felt a bit like a bird, with my breath creating the wind beneath my wings, enabling me to glide into the next "chapter" of pain in my writing – the chapter that forms the purpose of this book – my sexual abuse. As I moved between writing and pausing, with the pen moving around the figures of eight again, I felt a deep sense of peace within as I connected with an angel looking after me. Somehow, I knew that I had no need to fear and that, despite what I was writing about, I would be healed. I seemed to have shifted from being the river to being aware of the river and being able to watch it flow within me, flowing with it and yet outside of it at the same time.

Don't think and then hold back.

∞

Your daddy was damaged, so damaged, not even knowing he was. So was your mother but daddy was more damaged.

∞

Words about my father appeared in the front of my mind (I cannot recall the exact words). Suddenly and completely unexpectedly, I was transported back to the battlefield of my mind. I thought about what to write next, wondering whether or not I could put it down on paper, and questioning the validity of the source of what I wanted to write. Self-doubt and anxiety started to numb my soul again and I was thrown back into a thick mist of confusion and turmoil. I approached another cliff face in the river's path, but this time there seemed to be a tall, wide boulder standing upright at the edge of the cliff, stretching right across the riverbed, completely blocking the water's flow. It seemed that, as the water flowed into the boulder, the boulder increased in size to contain the water, creating an ever-deepening dam wall and creating a whirlpool within the dam. The whirlpool highlighted my circular thoughts: Can I write this? Can't I write this? My anxiety increased as the whirlpool created pressure on the dam wall and started to open a tiny crack in the boulder for the water to trickle through. I finally started writing and what I wrote remains engraved in my memory. The words "… but daddy was more damaged" contained a huge battle for me; a battle that remains with me even now as I write.

> I want to say goodbye for now, keep cycling. I will send you the people that will help you open your heart to me and what has happened, I have already.

∞

Love me just the way I am.

∞

I will protect you too.

After having written these words on the page, it was as if the river slowly started trickling back towards the ocean again, forming an estuary back to its source.

When I read the letter back to Louise, I felt as if I had returned to the calm, eternal depths of the ocean from where I had come. My pain seemed to have moved through me to finally release me back into the ocean, where I found stillness once more.

I shared with Louise the battle with my mind at the last dam wall. She explained to me that what I wanted to stop myself from writing was not a preconceived thought that was getting in the way, but it was rather a spontaneous flow from my unconscious that I was consciously blocking due to my fear and anxiety. She went on to explain that this was evident because it appeared towards the end of my letter, by which time I was in a state of "flow" with my unconscious, allowing the previous waterfalls to flow through my tears. While her explanation made rational sense to me, I was unable to quieten the part of me that did not want to hear what she had said. I was searching for any reason to doubt her professional judgement, and even doubted my own memory of her explanation. Clearly this was a territory that I did not want to move into.

After briefly glancing into this forbidden territory, I moved onto identifying any positive aspects that I could draw from the letter as a healing balm and a direction forward. I read through the letter again and felt that I was magnetically pulled towards the words: "... my courage is stronger than my fear ..."; "... you also have an angel looking after you – when you fall I will catch you and then you will learn to fly again and help others fly with your strong wings to help them with similar journeys to yours"; and "... you will return from this journey stronger than ever." I felt almost as if I was holding a compass in my hands in the form of this letter and all that I needed to do from there was to not let go of the compass and to use it when I felt that I was losing my sense of direction. Louise reflected back to me that the wise, inner child that had been writing this letter was actually a reflection of my soul. Louise had reflected exactly what my intuition was telling me – my wise, inner child is my soul.

A few years on, I can now reflect on how these three positive themes (my guardian angel, my courage being stronger than my fear, and my moving forwards into healing others) have formed a thread throughout my healing journey. They appeared in my letters of forgiveness at both retreats, as well as in both of the letters linked to projective imagery. They form the core of my healing process.

One of my biggest fears during my healing journey was that I would become completely emotionally overwhelmed, lose control and have to be hospitalised. I feared that my husband would lose his wife and that my son would lose his mother. I did not believe in my own strength and my own ability to access it on a spiritual level.

After the session with Louise had finished, while I was returning to reality over a cup of tea in the therapy room, I experienced an ever-expanding sense of deep inner peace and tranquillity. This peace felt similar to the peace I had felt while writing after the first waterfall of grief, during which I had moved from just being the river towards also being aware of the river. It seemed to be that part of myself that was controlling what the pen was writing, while at the same time enabling me to observe the writing from a more calm, safe, peaceful distance, rather than personally identifying with it and being fused with it emotionally. While I still felt as if I was about to become a trespasser on my own illegal territory, I somehow started to become aware that I could only be prosecuted by myself and therefore I was still in control. As my deep doubts and feelings of anxiety rolled through me, I briefly managed to find a place within myself where I no longer needed to engage in direct conflict with them. I let them come and go like leaves flowing with the current on the river's surface, while I remained relatively still within the depths of the river.

Cycling about 13 km home in the rain, mostly along muddy farm roads, grounded me back in reality. As I watched the front wheel turning around in front of me, I knew I still had a long journey ahead, but I was comforted by the rhythm of my heavy breathing and the circular motion of the pedals as I kept moving forward towards home. My progress was slow but consistent and seemed to reflect the circular motion of my healing process. Cycling acutely increased my awareness of my breathing. For more than forty years, I had been breathing without being fully alive; I had mostly been going through the motions of my life, numbed by a crippling past, and yet not being fully aware of it. As I reconnected with my love of cycling, I started to breathe my soul back to life.

Louise sent me a message later that day asking whether I had got home alright and I remember answering that I was all right; just tired, wet and muddy. The earth was healing me too!

13

THE DOOR TO MY UNCONSCIOUS DREAM WORLD RE-OPENS

Hazel

Warning from Louise

In this chapter Hazel describes in graphic detail the dreams she had over 20 years. Some of her dreams are sexually explicit and others have the quality of nightmares. This chapter is **not for sensitive readers**. If you would prefer not to read it, you could continue further on in this chapter, from the heading labelled *Healing*.

As Hazel mentions in this chapter, she was trained by a psychologist and used this knowledge to interpret her own dreams. Hazel's dreams brought new perspectives for her and played an important part in her healing journey, which is the reason this chapter was included in the book.

Should this chapter trigger you, I recommend you take the following steps immediately:

i) Breathe deeply 4-5 times

ii) Ground yourself by becoming aware of your body. Focus on all 5 your senses: identify 5 things you can hear, 4 things you can see, 3 things you can touch, 2 things you can smell and 1 thing you can taste

iii) Affirm/ reassure yourself for example "I am a survivor"; or "I can overcome this"

iv) Go for a walk, with someone to distract you for now

v) Seek professional support

Over a period of more than twenty years, I have come to realise that my dreams are not only an expression of my unconscious mind, but they have also provided me with a channel of communication from my soul, providing a voice for my lost, wounded inner child and guiding her healing. Over time, I have learnt to allow my soul to communicate with me through the voice of my dreams, sometimes surrendering to their revelations and at other times consciously requesting them not to reveal anything further regarding what has happened to me. In this way, I have learnt to consciously set the pace of my own healing process in my world of dreams.

Learning to interpret the language of my dreams has been foundational to my healing process. I am ever grateful to the clinical psychologist whom I saw about twenty years ago, for helping me to lay this foundation. As my healing journey with Louise progressed, I constantly referred back to dreams from the past that had already been explored in therapy with the clinical psychologist. In this way, we continually built upon those past dreams in making sense of the more recent dreams. All of these dreams spanned a time period of about twenty-six years.

I will begin by sharing and exploring the last dream that seemed to be the beginning of revealing the identity of my abuser.

I experienced the dream in September 2015, at a time when I was still unsure as to who had abused me. Reflecting on my dreams, I have realised that they expressed different aspects of my healing journey, through five themes: fear and terror, repressed trauma, dissociation, shame, and healing. After exploring the dream, I will take you on a journey through these dream themes. Finally, I will share a few more recent dreams that possibly reveal the identity of my abuser.

As I take you by the hand and journey together with you, I hope that you may be able to identify some of your own themes in the dream language speaking to you. However, please feel free to let go of my hand at any point and allow your dreams to take you on your own healing journey. Your soul will know when to hold my hand and when to let go, trusting your own, unique healing process through the world of your dreams.

THE DREAM:

I am sitting in a circle with a group of people and am experiencing a tremendous sense of fear, as I am aware of an invisible evil presence that is going to commit a serious crime against each person in the group. As my fear intensifies, I see a hand trying to grab one of the people. Then, suddenly, the face of a man flashes right in front of my face and, as I am totally consumed with fear, I scream "Help!"

At this point in the dream, my own screaming woke me up. When I awoke, I was sweating profusely and felt extremely anxious, consumed with fear and terror. The face had flashed by so quickly that I could only recall vague facial features – those of a white man, possibly with black/grey hair. I had no sense of what this man was going to do to me; just an overwhelming sense of something immensely evil from which I had no escape, and which might kill me through the intensity of my fear.

THE MEANING:

The circular arrangement of the people with whom I am sitting in the dream is an archetype of wholeness. It is a holistic symbol representing my whole, undivided, fully integrated sense of self. Each person represents a different aspect of myself; yet, sitting in a circle together, these different aspects of myself are connected and reconciled with each other through the central point in the circle. The sense of an invisible evil presence reveals my shadow – those aspects of myself that I fear confronting and of which I remain unconscious (hence they remain invisible to me). My increasing fear moving towards panic and terror and screaming on waking are paralleled in my snake dreams (explored under the theme of terror). As my panic reaches a peak, the face that flashes right in front of my face is the face of the person who abused me – but I am still not ready for him to be revealed fully to me – his facial features are unclear as he flashes past quickly, so as not to reveal his identity.

I had this dream the night after the intense therapy session with Louise that incorporated projective imagery and free association writing linked to my broken inner child. This dream was a turning point at which I chose to ask my dreams not to reveal anything further, as my fear of not being able to cope with parenting and work responsibilities started to overwhelm me. Since then, I have had a few dreams that possibly indicated the identity of my abuser, in which I have only experienced emotional detachment, but no longer dissociation. These are discussed towards the end of this chapter. My dreams were allowing my conscious mind to set the pace for my healing, soothing my fears while providing a sense of harmony between my mind and my soul.

Dream Themes:

Fear and terror:

Fear emerged in different forms – initially some dreams were of dogs about to be killed on a railway line as a train approaches, and a dead dog suddenly appearing in the water while I am swimming. (I have always associated dogs with my inner child – they represent innocence and unconditional love to me.) Fear was also revealed in dreams in which my personal space and body are being invaded: My bedroom is broken into and my drawer where my most sentimental possessions are kept is left open and empty. Furthermore, an arm reaches in through the window, unexpectedly touching my breasts while I am getting dressed in a rondawel (round hut) on the guest farm where we used to have family holidays when I was a young child.

The most commonly occurring symbol revealing terror over a period of ten years or more is that of a big black snake chasing me. I feel immensely helpless and powerless, never being able to get away from it, no matter what escape route I try (whether levitating into the air, climbing a tree or diving into a pool of water). As the snake gets closer to me, my fear escalates to terror and panic, and just before it catches me, I wake up, screaming, in a cold sweat and feeling immensely anxious.

While I never had a specific sense of what the snake would do to me when it caught me, I somehow knew that it would definitely kill me and that I had no power or ability to defend myself against it. These dreams were so terrifying that I always struggled to get back to sleep afterwards, and sometimes needed to turn the light on for a while to calm myself. My terror was so intense that, even having left these dreams in the past now, their impact remains close to me, like a shadow.

Some other images in which the snake appeared include a drawing and a clay model of a snake that I made at a Holotropic Breathwork workshop in 1993. (See Figures 3 and 4, Chapter 7.) We were given a lump of clay and asked to form it into any shape without allowing our preconceived thought processes to interfere with the process. I made a model of a large spitting cobra with its neck flared, about to attack, with a large hole in the clay just below the top of its head. I experienced an immense fear response when looking at the model afterwards, knowing that I had to move myself through the hole just below the snake's head. Once again, my terror was related to the fear that the snake was going to kill me. (See Figure 4.)

Another dream that was linked to the terrifying snake image, and that spoke to me during this period, is one in which I am having psychotherapy (with the therapist that I was seeing at that time) and she tells me that I need to face the terrifying snake. I reply that I am not ready, and then I am looking at an image of me drawing myself as a child and my father smacking me with a belt. I know that I am feeling very frightened of the belt but am detached emotionally as I watch myself draw this picture.

Yet another dream followed this just four days later. In that dream, my mother is talking to me openly about the fact that she and my father have had no sex life at all for a long time. I feel surprised that she is talking to me about this so openly. I am left wondering whether there is a link between these two dreams that may reveal the possible identity of my abuser.

I had another very powerful and terrifying experience one night in 1994, when I was trying to fall asleep in bed and I had a sense that a man with a big penis was approaching me. As he approached, I felt more and more terrified. I somehow managed to ask a friend I was living with to call my therapist, who came to the house in the middle of the night. I remember at first not really recognising my therapist, as she appeared to be a witch-like monster. She soon calmed me, and I managed to speak about my experience. Although this was not a dream as such, it left its big footprint on my journey through terror, as it was the only time in which my fear seemed to erupt into consciousness, yet with no specific memory – only the sheer terror of the image approaching me.

I would like to close this theme on terror by sharing with you a powerful source of healing during the time in which I was becoming overwhelmed with both grief over the loss of my foster mother and fear of the snake symbol. This was a psychic reading given to me by a clairvoyant whom I consulted. The essence of her message was that I needed to protect myself from the energy of the snake at that point in time and keep it at bay, as I first needed to "transcend Mother Earth" (deal with the grief over the physical loss of my foster mother and the emotional loss of my birth mother) before allowing the snake energy to emerge. She stressed that this was essential, in order to avoid a potentially major breakdown, as my aura was open and unprotected while I was dealing with transcending Mother Earth. I therefore needed to protect it from the snake. I was advised on how to do this by meditating on a huge white dome of light around my body, protecting me from the snake, and holding my hands in front of my solar plexus while meditating. I needed to ask my guardian angel for protection from the snake by tuning in to her love and serenity. Once protected from the snake, I was to visualise a big spider and draw near to it, become the spider, and see the world through the eyes of the spider, in order to move towards transcending Mother Earth. If the spider turned into anything other than the snake, I was to work with this image. I would be able to confront and then move onto befriending the snake only after having transcended Mother Earth. The psychic concluded by saying that I would be able to transcend both Mother Earth (the spider) and my sexual wounding (the snake) in this lifetime, and that the pain and trauma related to these is so deep because they have evolved over many lifetimes.

The archetypal symbol of the snake is woven into my writing throughout this book, as I believe it forms a thread symbolising my purpose in this life – that of sexual self-healing, moving towards the healing of others.

REPRESSED TRAUMA:

Repressed trauma expressed itself in only a few dreams, one of which I highlighted with a blue highlighter pen all those years ago. Although now faded on the page, it has never faded in my soul, as it was the first piece that I could place into the jigsaw puzzle of my healing years later.

THE DREAM:

I am listening to my mother, who is in a trance-like state, telling my father about my sexual abuse, and she says, "There was bleeding." Then my mother and my father are talking about my sexual abuse in front of me, although they are not aware that I am there. It is almost as if I am invisible to them in the dream. I feel emotionally upset and walk away crying, and an old friend comforts me. I know that I can't remember what happened in the abuse at all – it's almost as if I was knocked unconscious at the time. Then I say to my friend that there is no one to comfort me when I am feeling upset. He then replies, saying that I must go to my room. I don't want to go to my room, because I don't want to be alone. He finally says that I will not be alone, because I will be with my alarm clock.

THE MEANING:

My mother's trance-like state seemed necessary for her to break through her defences and enter an altered state of consciousness in order to talk about this. My invisibility and the fact that my parents were not aware that I was listening to their conversation left me with a sense that this conversation was something that I was not meant to hear – it was top secret. Clearly, both of my parents at the very least knew about my sexual abuse and were in some level of collusion over it. My old friend in the dream was an older male friend who had in many ways become a bit of a father figure to me. My sense of abandonment by my own father is revealed in my friend telling me to go to my room when

106

I am upset, rather than comforting me himself. My inability to remember my abuse reveals that this trauma has been completely repressed from consciousness. Being alone with the alarm clock is symbolic of my healing through time, through a process of this trauma re-awakening into consciousness. This is represented in the dream by my being awoken, from being unconscious in my sleep, by the alarm clock.

Other dreams included dreams about having a sense of urgency in needing to tell someone, as well as actually telling someone, that some kind of abuse has happened to me but that I can't remember what happened. I then go through a ritual or ceremony involving some form of abuse, but I can't remember what happens to me during the ritual. While going through this, I am holding onto a Yin-Yang symbol. I am then telling my therapist about my dream and reminding myself that I am not identified by my past, and that this happened to me a long time ago.

These dreams all reflect a past experience that has been banished from consciousness through repression – one of the most powerful defence mechanisms used by the psyche to cope with trauma (closely followed by the defence mechanism of dissociation).

DISSOCIATION:

The dreams involving dissociation occurred between 1993 and 2005 and, although only few and far between, they were the dreams that left me feeling most disturbed, due to their more explicit sexual content. On an emotional level, as well as on a physical level, I was completely split off from both my body and my emotions. I experienced myself as an observer outside of my body, watching what was happening in a clinical, objective, neutral, impartial, emotionally detached manner, almost as a researcher doing a science experiment. The most disturbing of these dreams occurred in 1994, the year following the Holotropic Breathwork workshop in which I created the clay snake model and the snake drawings.

THE DREAM:

I am looking at a little penis and I don't know whose penis it is, as it is just the penis that I can see. The penis starts increasing in size and then I hear a mechanical voice saying "in" and then "out". I can't remember what happened then, but the next thing I know is that there are broken bits of penis coming out of my vagina on the "out" call. It's as if these broken bits of penis are somehow being forced out of me by the mechanical voice that I am hearing. I am observing and hearing this scene from somewhere outside of my body and I am completely emotionally detached as if I am observing something that could be happening to someone else, although I know it is me.

THE MEANING:

This dream perhaps comes closest to possibly revealing what actually happened to me – I was either raped or someone repeatedly inserted some kind of object into my vagina. I think the fact that I dissociated in this dream possibly reflects that this was my way of coping when this actually happened to me – my mind slipped away and escaped by separating from my body to a safe place, as a way of protecting myself from overwhelming fear, pain and trauma. I was not yet ready to identify my abuser – hence the penis is not attached to a person I can see. Even the voice that I hear is a mechanical voice – unattached to anyone and devoid of emotion or tone, and yet it is telling me what is happening. The fact that I cannot remember what happened next is possibly due to the fact that this was the point at which I was initially penetrated – it was too traumatic to remember, but it was evidenced by the next thing I saw – broken bits of penis coming out of my vagina.

Other dreams in which I was in a dissociated state include a dream I had in 1993. In the dream, I am lying down and observing an axe wavering around the area of my vagina, with the sharp, cutting edge pointing towards me. No one is holding the axe, which is swinging in the open air on its own. While the axe is not being pushed into me or hurting me at all, I am feeling sexually aroused and am judging myself to be sexually perverted for being sexually aroused by this.

Twelve years later, in 2005, I had another dream, in which I saw a clear image of a long penis being put into someone's small mouth. Again, I am not able to identify whose penis it is or whose mouth it is, as I only see the penis and the mouth, again unattached to anyone. While I am watching this scene as an external observer, relatively uninvolved and detached from it, I am aware somehow that I do not like what I am seeing. Although this is not a dissociative dream as such, I do not remember that it was me in the dream. I experienced watching it in an emotionally detached manner.

On browsing through these dreams in my old dream records now, I am once again quite astounded, experiencing an only-too-familiar feeling of: "Oh my God, this must have happened to me." This brings to mind another dream in which I go to see a gynaecologist for a check-up for physical evidence of rape. No evidence is found except for some "watered down" faeces. I am then asked whether I have recently been swimming, to which I reply, "yes". This seems to indicate that physical bodily evidence may have been lost over time.

This has been the most challenging section to write in this chapter on my dream world, and I have called Louise in tears, just trying to write my way through my grief and tears once again. I want to thank you for sharing it with me.

SHAME:

Shame became the lens through which I saw myself – worthless and inadequate, with something inherently bad in me. It was often accompanied by a feeling of deadness inside me – an emotional vacuum of numbness and depression. Shame of my sexual body is primarily what was expressed through my dreams, but guilt and a sense of personal inadequacy also featured strongly. In reading through my dreams now, I am struck by a dream that speaks of both guilt and of my deep shame of my body.

THE DREAM:

I am my present age but am staying with my foster mother in her house. I do not feel much emotional connection to my foster mother. There does not seem to be a mother-child bond of love between us, but I am not sure why this is the case. I return to my bedroom to find that I have left my duvet and sheets covered in my own menstrual blood, and my dirty sanitary pad is on the floor. I feel deeply ashamed of myself and I am embarrassed, wondering whether my foster mother has been into my room in my absence and has seen this. I then begin to wonder whether my foster mother's family will eat meals together and whether I will be welcome to join them at mealtime. I feel somehow that I cannot just help myself to their food, and I am then worried about how I will get food when I am hungry. I feel very alone and alienated from her family.

THE MEANING:

In the dream, I am in my foster mother's house where, in reality, I was loved as a very young baby. However, despite this, there is little love between us in the dream. Although I am not sure why the love bond between us seems absent, the dream then goes on to reveal the reason. Somehow, my sexuality is dirty (the bloody mess), and this is my fault, and I am to blame for it. (I left the bloody mess on the bed and on the floor.) The dream expresses my deeply intense bodily shame as a sexual woman. Furthermore, it clearly speaks of my sense of worthlessness and therefore being undeserving of love. (I am not welcome to eat meals with the family or share their food – food is symbolic of love in this dream.) The dream reveals how my feelings of guilt (for having left the bloody mess in the bedroom) become transformed into feelings of deep shame. (I am a worthless and unlovable person.) Blaming myself for my abuse became my only way of coping as a child. I thought that it had to be my fault, as I could not cope with the trauma and grief of being abused. As I was at my present age in the dream, it reveals how I have carried this guilt and shame into my adulthood.

On reflecting on my dreams now, I can see a pattern in which my feelings of guilt or sense of personal inadequacy regarding things I had done wrong or incompetently were later followed by more dreams of bodily and sexual shame.

Dreams of guilt include those in which I am being reprimanded for having done something wrong and yet not realising at the time that what I have done is wrong. It seems to be in the process of being reprimanded or disciplined that I realise that I must have been guilty. (These also include dreams in which I am reprimanded for taking too much food.) Another recurring dream is one in which I have to go back to school to repeat the exams of my final high school year. Despite knowing that I have already passed these exams with a good grade, I am somehow sure that I need to pass again with a better grade. (This reveals my feelings of not being a good enough person, no matter what I achieve – my sense of self-worth had become linked to my achievements.)

Other dreams that spoke of bodily shame included one in which I am menstruating and cannot control the heavy flow of blood that is running down my legs, staining my trousers and the floor, and leaking into the bath water. I feel very dirty and deeply ashamed, with a sense of self-loathing and disgust at myself. No matter what I do, I cannot get myself clean. Other much more recent dreams included dreams of me not being able to control my faeces. In one dream, I know that something bad has just happened to me, but I cannot remember what has happened. I then pass my faeces in the toilet. I just can't control the continual flow of my faeces that results in the toilet overflowing, regardless of how many times I try to flush the toilet. In another dream, I am lying sick in bed and I do not know what the cause of my illness is. I look up towards the wall above my bed and I see a patch of my own faeces smeared on the wall. While still feeling ashamed, I am somehow a little more emotionally detached in these recent dreams. I think that, in these dreams, my faeces symbolise my deep sense of personal and bodily shame.

Looking back, I can now begin to see my own healing progress on my journey through shame. This is revealed in how my earlier dreams only indicate guilt, self-loathing and deep bodily shame. My later dreams reveal that something has happened to me prior to feeling this shame and that it has been the cause of my shame, and the intensity of my shame becomes more subdued (e.g. I am sick, but I don't know the cause of my illness, and something happened prior to my uncontrolled faeces overflowing in the toilet).

Shame defined me in the past, but more recently, as I have been able to interpret its language in my dreams, I have begun to release my imprisoned soul and to start flying towards freedom.

HEALING:

While browsing through my dreams and linking them to the four themes that Louise had helped me identify, I was astounded to realise that the strongest and clearest theme emerging through my dreams was the theme of healing. Ironically, this theme became apparent only while searching for the other dreams. I had overlooked the purpose behind my journey: my healing; the other side of my pain. Throughout the past twenty years or more, my dreams have continually reflected the circular nature of my healing process, with many powerfully healing dreams occurring between early dreams of terror and dissociation. They seemed to be laying a foundation of strength, helping me to manage the next layer of pain being revealed. This is the circular language of my soul speaking, as it has also inspired me with powerfully healing songs both before and after encountering immense challenges on my path.

Now, looking more closely at the dates and chronology of these dreams, I can begin to identify my own healing progress in the changes from symbolism towards realism (e.g. the axe and the snake are replaced by the penis). Most significantly, my healing is also evidenced through the changes from a state of dissociation towards a state of being centred in myself, and through my dreams revealing more specific sexual content. Furthermore, I am now able to see how I have moved from feeling deeply disturbed and ashamed of these dreams (thinking that perhaps I was sexually perverted in some way) towards allowing them to speak to me about what has happened to me and, ultimately, to heal me.

Flying was the primary symbol of healing, especially in my earlier dreams. I would realise that I could levitate to lift myself off the ground and then fly over whatever was obstructing my path. Flying was not only immensely liberating on an emotional level, but it was also spiritually healing. My body would start to feel lighter and almost no longer physical, as I became more a part of my aura (the energy field around my body). Having reached a high altitude, I would then rise through a line of white light, beyond which there was a beautiful scene of blue skies and empty space into which I would fly. I intuitively knew that I have always been able to fly, ever since I was young, and expressed this to my brother in one dream in which he says to me, "You really fear transcending Mother Earth" (Mother Earth being the feminine aspects of myself – related to the loss of my foster mother, my wounding by my biological mother, and my sexual wounding). I somehow know that this is one of my greatest fears and challenges, and yet I know I can fly and always have been able to. A more recent dream of flying is one I experienced in 2005. In the dream, I am flying with a sexual partner. As we are flying, he starts to penetrate me, and I calmly tell him that I do not want to make love, as I am not on the contraceptive pill. After that, we continue flying while mutually masturbating each other. The atmosphere is highly sensual, peaceful, calm and loving – a tremendously healing space in our sexual flight together.

Emotional catharsis in my dreams was another form of healing medicine. In one dream, I am reunited with my foster mother and cry in her arms as she cradles me like a baby, and a video of me as a young child comes to life. As I speak to the child that is me, I see the deep sadness in her eyes and want to weep as my adult self.

Dreams also offered a channel through which my sexual body could speak to me – revealing, releasing and healing the secret it has had to hold throughout most of my life. The first dream I had in 1994 was a dream that has also been carried into my early sexual fantasies, leaving me with a deep, soul-destroying sense of shame, not only over my sexual body, but also over my very sense of being a sexual woman. In this dream, I am being hit very hard (smacked or lashed) by somebody for something I have done wrong. My body reacts with severe pain deep inside my vagina – it is like a deep throbbing pain that feels like something is about to explode inside of me (like a bad orgasm of some kind). I wake up with this intense pain in my vagina. When the pain subdues, I realise that I have released some vaginal fluid and that I have also experienced some level of sexual arousal, although it was mostly painful. This sexual bodily reaction has been with me for a long time, mostly on the level of a sexual fantasy. Similarly, in another dream, I am telling an old school friend that I have something like a "headache" in my vagina. This is of great concern to me and I have no idea why I have this condition. I speak about it intellectually to her, feeling emotionally detached. I have mostly tried to make sense of this as some kind of sexualisation of my emotional abuse, but this did not relieve my deeper sense of bodily shame. Furthermore, the sexual dreams outlined already, in which I was completely dissociated, involved me waking up with these sensations of pain and pleasure in my vagina too.

Recently, I was searching the internet on the psychology behind sadomasochistic sexual fantasies. My tears started flowing down my face when I read that, while there may be other causes, this was not an uncommon response for victims of sexual abuse. My tears released both tremendous sadness and a strong sense of relief. I realised that I was not sexually perverted or a sadomasochist by my inherent nature; I was both a victim and a survivor of sexual abuse. This realisation was immensely healing for me on all levels – mind, body and soul. Finally, my body spoke, not only of its sexual pain but also of its sexual healing, in a dream in which I say to someone that I am scared of men. I am then lifted into the air by two invisible hands. My body starts to feel very light and, as I slowly move up and down in the air, supported by these hands, I experience a wonderful orgasm. Again, there is a strong spiritual element in this dream, as my body is lifted and starts to feel lighter – there is a sense that I am able to defy gravity and transcend my own fears.

My healing was also expressed in the way in which my terror of the snake moved towards a sense of being able to confront it. This was revealed quite literally in a dream in which I see the snake and look it directly in the eyes. Although the snake is a little distance away from me, it is not chasing me and I feel no fear or terror, but rather an immense sense of personal empowerment and inner strength. A much more recent snake dream is one in which I am carrying this snake in a closed black plastic bag and it is asleep. As the snake awakens, I begin to feel fear and terror of what it will do to me. Then I am standing in a group of people, watching the snake. I want to kill it with my gun so that it can't harm me, but a vet tells me not to do that and shows me how to inject it with a sedative, rendering it powerless to hurt me. I watch in amazement as the vet does this, and then I ask him whether the injection will hurt the snake. He replies that it doesn't hurt the snake but that you have to get very close to the snake first, in order to give it the injection. He then tells me that the skill lies in the manner in which you approach the snake before injecting it.

In these dreams, I am regaining my sense of personal power, as well as beginning to show some level of compassion towards the snake. (After wanting to kill it, I realise that I don't necessarily want to hurt it or kill it; I just need to learn what to do to ensure that it cannot hurt me.) The healing power in these dreams lay in realising my own ability to confront the snake. Despite my fear, I was going to be able to confront the snake and, in doing so, would disempower it. I knew what this dream was telling me

– I was now finally going to be able to confront my own sexual abuse and, in doing so, heal from it.

Another powerful healing dream incorporating the snake is one in which an old friend of mine is showing me a model of a big snake that she has made. As she removes each layer of skin, another more beautifully painted layer is revealed beneath the old one. The snake is coiled up and she shows me the tail and then helps me to find its head. I am at peace with the snake in this dream.

One dream I had in 2005 brought me forward in time to the first St. Raphael's Sanctuary Healing Retreat during which I painted a huge tree with enormously strong roots on the "Who am I?" box. In the dream, I become a huge tree with immensely strong roots that strengthen the tree as they continue to grow deeper and deeper into the earth. I speak to myself, saying "I am very old, incredibly strong and wise." The symbol of the tree's roots seemed to be offering me the courage and strength that I needed to grow through my personal pain towards healing myself and others.

Other dreams showing my healing progress include one or two in which I am with a large group of people at a social gathering or party and I initially feel that I cannot eat the food provided. I then eat lots of food, enjoying it with the other people, and then celebrate with them by dancing and singing. These dreams show how my sense of self-esteem has grown towards a sense of knowing that I am deserving of love and emotional nourishment (symbolised by food), rather than being inherently unworthy of these.

Finally, I would like to share with you my most spiritual dream, which I had back in 1993 while at the Holotropic Breathwork workshop, and which then returned to me in my sleep during a recent afternoon nap. At both of these times, I was experiencing different levels of deep, emotional pain. In the dream, I am looking into the face of Jesus Christ and my whole being becomes immersed in a strong sense of eternal peace, love and serenity, as I seem to become enveloped in the white light that surrounds His face. This image is now engraved on my soul as a sanctuary to return to whenever I feel the need to regain my peace and healing.

MORE RECENT DREAMS:

Other recent dreams include those that point towards my father being responsible for my sexual abuse. In the first dream, I am attending a Holotropic Breathwork workshop, during which I am in an altered state of consciousness and I am weeping over some loss related to my father, but I do not know specifically what has happened with him to cause my immense grief. The person who is coordinating the workshop is one of my old high school teachers. Upon reflecting on this dream, I remembered that I had experienced a mental fantasy of this teacher either physically hurting me by hitting me in some way and/or pushing me almost beyond physical exhaustion. (She was my athletics teacher.) The fantasy was accompanied by a response in which I felt a combination of pain and pleasure in my sexual body. This dream was pointing towards confirming that my father may have sexually abused me in some way. This was being revealed through my bodily response to my projective fantasy with the teacher – hence my overwhelmingly deep sense of grief over my father.

In a second dream, I am telling my father that I have pain in my genitals but, despite this, he starts touching me on my genitals, only making the pain worse. I then watch him lying on the floor with only his underpants on, moving up and down in a sexual motion as if making love with someone, but there is no one lying underneath him. I am emotionally detached in this dream, as if I am watching a film scene, but I am still centred in my body, rather than being dissociated.

I recall sharing these dreams with Louise and initially experiencing a short-but-intense mental battle and an increased level of anxiety as I explored the possibility that the dreams may indicate that my father could have been the person who had sexually abused me. I clearly remember, as if it was yesterday, both my tremendous sadness and a sense of my sanity returning to me as I finally allowed myself to acknowledge this possibility. Despite there being no definite evidence or memory recall, my deep sadness, tears and relief from anxiety were the only truth I knew.

Looking back, I now realise how divine providence must have been guiding the process of healing through my world of dreams. Two of my most significant dissociative dreams from 1993 and 2005 had been written on separate pieces of paper (now browned with age) and stapled into the front of my dream book (which must have been unavailable to me when I recorded the dreams). What is the probability of me not having lost these pieces of paper and/or the books of recorded dreams from more than twenty years ago; dreams that proved to be foundational in making sense of my present dreams?

Now, as I near completion of this chapter on dreams, I am no longer desperately searching through my old dreams or my recent ones for an answer to the question of who abused me sexually. While I am much closer to answering that question, I am also much closer to finding peace and healing regardless of the answer. Most significantly, however, my dreams have provided me with a deep sense of peace and of knowing that I have always been able to heal myself. I will therefore continue to grow and heal, irrespective of which questions remain unanswered.

In this context, a memory springs to mind now that I would like to share with you: I was at a critical point in my healing journey and Louise had recommended that I see a psychiatrist to get medication for my anxiety. She had also suggested that I meditate regularly during the period in which I was waiting to see the clinical psychologist whom she had referred me to. (My anxiety levels were escalating out of control as I battled with my suspicions regarding who had abused me. At the same time, I was experiencing unexpected, intense reactions to everyday situations that triggered immense anxiety, and these were starting to leave me feeling incapacitated.) As I was standing in a long queue at the local state clinic, I received a quote from Louise on my cell phone. As I read it, I started to feel a deep sense of remembering coming over me, as if I was being reminded of something crucial to my healing process; something that I innately knew but had completely lost sight of. I was no longer aware of the noise and chaos around me as a silence filled me with a profound sense of peace – this quote was speaking the language of my soul: "Don't search for the answers, which could not be given to you now, because you would not be able to live with them. And the point is to live everything. Live the questions now. Perhaps then, some-day far in the future, you will gradually, without even noticing it, live your way into the answer" (Rainer Maria Rilke). I can now look back and see how this had started to manifest in my healing journey.

Finally, I would like to draw your attention more closely again to how my healing dreams have almost formed a safety net for me throughout my dream world. They have been holding me in a safe place, enabling me to surrender to my fears being expressed and released through my dreams of terror, shame, dissociation and repressed trauma. My dreams have always been a channel through which not only my unconscious voice but also the voice of my soul can be heard; my soul that always knows and reminds me of the other side of my pain – my healing.

Thank you for sharing my journey with me through my dreams. I hope that you have been able to find yourself somewhere along my journey. If it has been in any way helpful in enabling you to listen to the voice of your soul through your own dream language, allowing it to take you by the hand on your unique healing journey through the world of your dreams, then my purpose in writing this chapter has been fulfilled.

Note from Louise:

A range of books are available on dream interpretation describing a number of techniques. As an occupational therapist I have NOT been trained in the interpretation of dreams.

I do believe dreams are a door to our unconscious world and can bring incredible wisdom and insights. I would therefore encourage you to keep a dream journal. However, as this falls outside my scope of practice as an occupational therapist, I suggest you find a psychologist (or some life coaches) who have been trained to guide you in the interpretation of your dreams.

14

LIAISING WITH ANXIETY

Hazel

Although my world of dreams was moving me towards healing, I continued to struggle with my anxiety, which was now being made more manageable with the use of antidepressants. My anxiety seemed to be directly related to my spontaneously emerging grief and sadness whenever I allowed myself to contemplate the hypothetical possibility that my father had sexually abused me. My emotions emerged quite uncontrollably as a fountain of tears from a deep underground spring, leaving me emotionally exhausted and mentally confused. This resulted in further anxiety. I was starting to feel helplessly trapped in a whirlwind of escalating anxiety from which I could not escape – I could not see an exit door. This intense battle between my head and my heart needed to find a resolution, and yet I sensed that no peace was to be found while I remained on this battlefield. However, with the help of medication, I slowly began to be able to feel some rare moments of stillness at the centre of the whirlwind. It was a centre from which I could see the exit door from my anxiety, and from which I could more quietly notice and observe my emotional reactions of grief and sadness. I needed to find a way to stay in this centre of stillness, but it was no easy task.

Louise initially asked me to do some relaxation breathing exercises and then tried to move me onto visualising my anxiety. Unfortunately, I cannot recall my response to this, as it was a long time ago and I am unable to remember all aspects of the session clearly. Following on from this, Louise asked me to put the battle between my head and heart onto paper by writing down all my feelings and thoughts, without thinking, and by using the free association writing technique. What I wrote next is presented below.

∞

I feel like it is my fault that I have let you down, I feel guilty for even thinking that you could have done this to me?? I feel so sad when I think that my feelings could be because you did do something to me.

∞

I am sorry for even thinking this but I know that I am not making up my feelings when I allow myself to think this.

∞

I am not the one going mad, I don't want to think this of you. I don't care if you die because you just confuse me.

∞

You know about this and you are a lying bastard – whatever you know – **TELL ME**.

At first, I struggled so much with my thoughts that I was unable to even start writing anything, and my pen just kept on moving around repeatedly in the figure of eight, as the movement seemed to reflect my endless circular thoughts trapped at the outer edges of a tornado. Somehow, I was briefly drawn a little way inwards from the outer edges as I wrote about my feelings and was then pushed back outwards by my thoughts.

As my anger started to emerge and there was some small release from my guilt, I briefly allowed myself to be drawn inwards from the outer edges, only to be thrown back outwards by my thoughts, and I once again started forming the figures of eight.

Finally, as I finished my writing, my anger gave me the strength to pull myself much closer towards the centre of the tornado – the source of its power. While I still didn't find stillness and peace there, I did find some strength and courage in my anger, and I managed to complete my writing.

As I read what I had written to Louise, I felt a little calmer, almost as if the distance between me and what I was reading created a sense of calmness, despite its content and details. I felt like I was moving towards the exit door from my anxiety.

After reading what I had written, I was asked to have a conversation with my anxiety on paper, using the left-and right-handed journaling technique. The questions I wrote using my right hand, and the answers I received through writing with my left hand, are presented below, together with my reflections on the content.

Q: What does this feeling mean when I think about you or if you did this to me?
A: It means

As I tried to fill the blank space appearing below the first question, I started to feel intensely anxious. The more I tried to push the anxiety away to see what I could write in the blank space, the faster and more ferociously it bounced back to me. I started to feel blinded by a threatening sense of panic that almost blurred my vision of the first two words of the unfinished answer on the page in front of me.

Q: What does the anxiety mean, what's the purpose of the anxiety?
A: To protect and defend from feeling what is too threatening.

As I answered the second question, a seed started to germinate somewhere deep inside me. Some of the first-year psychology theories that I had learnt as a student more than twenty years ago suddenly started to manifest in my own life in my answer. However, this time my answer was most definitely not being learnt from a book. Seeds cannot grow without the life-giving water of personal experience.

Q: **Can you get the hell out of my way?**
A: I will try, you must be patient.

I clearly remember Louise then asking me to write down what I wanted to ask my anxiety to do next. Both my question and answer came without any hesitation.

Q: **What needs to happen before you will be ready?**
A: I need to know that I have already survived you doing this to me. I need to feel that I am stronger than you.

After having written the first sentence in answer to the question, Louise asked me to start the next sentence with the words, "I need to feel" and then complete the sentence myself. She was trying to shift me away from my thoughts towards connecting me more with my heart and/or soul.

Q: **Where do I get this stronger feeling from?**
A: My spirit.

My pen flowed spontaneously into my answer to the next question. I was standing just in front of the exit door to my anxiety, looking straight ahead through the open door.

Q: **How do I join my feelings to my spirit?**
A: Meditate and pray and ask for strength.

As I wrote down the answer to the last question, I walked confidently through the exit door. I finally recalled that I had known this answer all the time, but I had simply forgotten the part of me that knew the answer. I felt a huge sense of relief and peace at last. I knew exactly what I needed to do to enable me to allow my anxiety to flow through me, rather than overwhelm me. I had once again come home to my soul.

This was another turning point – the beginning of a new pathway into the chapters ahead in this book. I was at the start of a journey towards being reunited with the ultimate source of healing – God or spirit (or whatever terminology feels right for you).

READER'S REFLECTION:

When you are feeling emotionally overwhelmed, out of control, and unable to see a way out of your intense emotional distress, try to create even just a short space of uninterrupted time in which you do something that you know has worked for you in the past, to connect you with your True self or soul – that part of you that can allow the emotion to come, and then let it go, rather than becoming totally identified and fused with it. This is different for everyone – it could be drawing, painting, engraving, singing, or writing – whatever channel works for you. It does not need to be the left- and right-handed journaling technique, although it was very effective for me. Now you can enter into a dialogue with your soul about the problem you are dealing with and ask that the answers that you need in order to find peace will be revealed to you in some way through this activity. They may not be immediate, and they may come in disguise, but you will reveal your own answers that will be unique to you, as you have always known these answers.

15

REFLECTIONS ON LIAISING WITH ANXIETY

Louise

Within the traditional medical model, anxiety and depression are seen as undesirable symptoms that need to be treated and "dealt with", as they cause people discomfort and render them dysfunctional. During my own journey, when I found my belief that "nothing is coincidental in our lives" and that our life's journey is primarily about developing our soul and developing a relationship with God, it necessitated that I reconsider my thoughts on anxiety and depression. More and more, I became convinced that depression is a sign of spiritual awakening, providing an opportunity for the True Self to show itself. I was still unsure about anxiety. However, with my belief that the soul knows so much more than we can even comprehend, I wanted to explore in more depth what the possible "purpose" of anxiety could be.

On Hazel's journey, she would often send me a WhatsApp message in the early morning, saying that she was feeling overwhelmed by anxiety and asking to be excused from her work. The anxiety was always preceded by an event in her life, e.g. her father making contact with her, or her having had a dream of a sexual nature. Her anxiety was disabling her. Traditional methods of breathing and relaxation techniques were not being effective, and I decided to be brave and explore Hazel's anxiety through her soul's perspective.

The session was held at her home and we were alone. Hazel's anxiety level was high and, as is typical with anxiety, she was restless. We did some deep breathing exercises and then I gave Hazel an exercise to visualise anxiety. I asked her to imagine anxiety as a person and to take a good look at anxiety: What did he/she/it look like? What did it say or do? How did it walk or talk? I don't recall much about her reaction. Following on from this, I asked Hazel to simply write down all her feelings that related to her battle with anxiety, using the free association writing technique. After this, something at that stage prompted me to try another technique. As I mentioned previously, in order to access the wisdom of our soul or our True Self, we need to be grounded, to connect to our soul, and to allow our soul a conduit in some way (whether writing or painting, etc.) to express itself. I decided to try the left- and right-handed journaling technique in order to start a dialogue between Hazel and her soul, around her anxiety. Hazel was instructed to write questions to her soul around the topic of her anxiety, using her dominant right hand. When the question had been written, she needed to change the colour of her pen and switch hands, answering the question with her non-dominant hand (in Hazel's case, her left hand) without thinking or pre-empting the answer.

Hazel initially struggled with the dialogue and showed some resistance. I encouraged her to stick at it. What emerged was incredible! In a nutshell, Hazel's soul conveyed the following: the anxiety was described as the bodyguard of her ego. If an event was perceived as being too threatening to the ego, the bodyguard (i.e. her anxiety) would kick in to protect Hazel's ego. The event was seen as threatening to a false belief of the ego, for example, "I am not able to deal with my life at the moment. It is all too much for me. I'm going to go crazy and lose my job." Knowing and believing that we are spiritual beings, we know that in essence nothing can happen to us that can add to or destroy our spiritual nature. We are spiritual beings, but our ego is bound in "reality". The image created in the dialogue was literally that her bodyguard was coming out to defend her and was throwing its weight around. Even more amazingly, within the dialogue, the soul advised her to spend more time in meditation, in order to strengthen her soul or True Self. It promised that if she became more aware of her soul, she would not be caught up in "reality", but she would remember who she truly was (a spiritual being loved by God) and that nothing could ever happen to her that would change this truth. If she knew this unequivocally and believed it, her perspective on the event would be changed and anxiety would not be needed to defend her ego. She would also know how to manage her anxiety when it did show up. Her soul knew how to let it come and then let it go, rather than fusing with it and thus becoming overwhelmed by it. The anxiety was serving a specific purpose. It was not something to just "get rid of" or to be seen as superfluous or undesirable; it had a specific purpose.

It was the first time, in working with a client, that I had been brave enough to venture so far out from my traditional training rooted in the medical model, and to specifically dialogue with anxiety. The result is that I can never again view anxiety and depression as "bad" experiences that need to be "removed". I believe that they are signs, or rather a message, of something happening on a deeper level; they serve a purpose, and we need to listen to their message. If we don't, we will miss it, slap a label on people and medicate them, without affording them the opportunity to understand what is actually happening. More importantly, that will deny them the opportunity to find the best means of moving past the anxiety.

Since then, I have used this method with other clients, at times using the psychodrama technique where anxiety is personified, instead of the left- and right-handed journaling technique. In the psychodrama technique, people talk to their anxiety, using the role reversal technique. It appears that each client's use of anxiety differs, and that anxiety is not always necessarily a bodyguard for the ego. One client, who suffered from both anxiety and depression, revealed that her anxiety had become a type of companion, something that made her feel more alive in some way, in contrast to her depression, which deprived her of all feeling. The wisdom she tapped into revealed that her anxiety would leave her as soon as she realised that she did not really need the anxiety in order to feel alive. In her case, her anxiety decreased significantly when she understood this, because she stopped "fighting" her anxiety; instead, she welcomed it.

I am eternally grateful to Hazel for being brave enough and for trusting me enough to try this approach without knowing the outcome. Without this experience, I would still be postulating and surmising about the role of anxiety and depression in mental health clients. Now I can assure my clients that they are not crazy or abnormal, and that the anxiety comes bringing a message.

READER'S REFLECTION:

Instead of seeing emotions, especially strong or overwhelming emotions, as being threatening or abnormal, welcome them and take time to listen to their messages. Each one serves a specific purpose. Listen to the emotions and their messages, so that you can understand, learn and grow beyond them.

16

ASK AND YOU SHALL RECEIVE

Hazel

"I've got the joy, joy, joy, joy down in my heart, down in my heart, down in my heart. I've got the joy, joy, joy, joy down in my heart, down in my heart to stay" (George Willis Cooke)

For a while after liaising with my own anxiety using the left- and right-handed journaling technique, I tried to follow my new-found insights by making a structured time in my day to meditate. As nearly always happens, I was not successful with creating that regular undisturbed time, as my will to stay in bed seemed stronger than my will to get up earlier in the morning! (There was very little other free time in my day, apart from that at the end of the day after Joshua was asleep, when I was usually ready to sleep too, rather than to meditate.) Instead, I tried "stealing" time wherever I possibly could in the natural course of my daily routines ... while driving to work after having dropped Joshua off at preschool; while stacking the dishwasher; or while walking Chequer, our adorable ridgeback, on the farm.

I recall, as if it was yesterday, walking with Chequer on the farm one day, on one of the few occasions that Joshua did not join me. I had my solitude, being accompanied only by Chequer, and my cell phone in my pocket had been set on silent. As I looked up at the beautiful mountains on the horizon, I silently asked God to release me from my seemingly never-ending mental and emotional turmoil regarding who it was who had sexually abused me. I specifically asked that I be left with no further doubt over this, despite not wanting to regain a conscious memory for fear of becoming overwhelmed. As I continued walking, the old children's gospel song "I've got the joy, joy, joy, joy down in my heart" spontaneously came to mind. As I started singing it, the words changed to "I've got the peace that passes understanding down in my heart," as if someone else had changed the words for me! This slight change in lyrics was not at all preconceived. Initially, it felt as if the song was flowing through me, but as I continued singing, I almost experienced a sense that I was becoming the song, rather than just acting as a channel for the song. The message of the song was enveloping my whole being in immense peace and tranquillity, beyond what I can now find the words to describe.

At some point while walking and singing, a thought entered my mind: the thought that I needed to find some old pictures and pieces of writing that I had done back in the early 1990s when I was a psychology honours student. Again, this thought kept coming back to me repeatedly. It was almost as if it was being printed into every footprint I was making. As I walked along singing, I could almost "hear" this thought harmonising with the song's melody, as they merged in my soul.

Later that evening, after Joshua was asleep, I started looking for my old pictures and written pieces. It did not take too long, as I knew where I had stored them. After finding my old pictures, I started to go through another file with all of my old writing in it. The file was in my office, only a few metres away from the desk where I was now writing this book. I calmly paged through the written passages that, despite being more than twenty years old, somehow still felt very familiar. My sense of calm remained with me until I started reading a free association letter that I had written to my father. It felt as if the ground on which I was standing was starting to cave in from under me as I read the letter:

131

Warning from Louise

What follows is the letter written by Hazel that contains strong language as well as a sexually explicit picture she drew. This is **not for sensitive readers** and may trigger people who have been through similar experiences. The reason we have decided to keep the letter and picture in the book is three-fold. Firstly, it is a crucial part of the story. In this letter and picture the only two questions Hazel was seeking answers for regarding her sexual abuse, is found. Secondly, this again supports understanding that *our souls know* so much more than we are aware of, and we hope to encourage others to be more in tune with their soul, as our souls often can lead us to find the path to healing. Lastly, we exist in a culture that wants to silence and turn a blind eye to the discomfort surrounding sexual abuse. By not including this picture, we felt that we would be perpetuating the unhealthy culture. As uncomfortable as this may be to many readers, it is only when we become brave enough to bring light into the darkness, that true healing for our culture can begin. This picture is a sad reality for far too many abused survivors.

Should you choose not to read the letter or look at the picture, you can continue reading the Reflection at the end of the chapter or start at the beginning of Chapter 17.

Should this trigger you, I recommend you take the following steps immediately:

i) Breathe deeply 4-5 times

ii) Ground yourself by becoming aware of your body. Focus on all 5 your senses: identify 5 things you can hear, 4 things you can see, 3 things you can touch, 2 things you can smell and 1 thing you can taste

iii) Affirm/ reassure yourself for example "I am a survivor"; or "I can overcome this".

iv) Go for a walk, with someone to distract you, for now

v) Seek professional support

Dear father –

I love you, I hate you, I want to kill you, smash you to bits
and swim in your blood. I am riddled with guilt. I want to
kill myself. I am too emotional, illogical – I can't be logical
because I am a <u>woman</u>. What's the point in trying to love you
when I am filled with RAGE that gets killed before it's born.
Oh God – What do I do now – I just want to end everything.
I can't blow bubbles, I can't play – what's the point???/??

Yes – of course you are always there for me – that's called
ignoring me in your language.

No !!! – I fucking don't want your love.

Life carries on – I need a roof over my head and food – why?

No – of course I DON'T UNDERSTAND.

FUCK
YOU

Every day I am psychoanalyzed to try and get you out of my
mind –

In – out – in
Out-in-out-in
Out-in-out
Push harder –
harder – harder
I want to scream – I can't
In – out
In-out-in-out
I need a roof and food – what for?

I want to be there to put a flower on your grave, mommy – to say good-bye 'cos I never said goodbye to you properly – maybe that's why I must have a roof and food – to say goodbye to you

NO – I'M FEELING
SORRY FOR MYSELF

Hush little baby – please don't cry – mommy's gonna buy you a rocking bird and if that rocking bird don't sing, the witch will buy you a fuck.

Please just die – my life would be a haven – BOTH OF YOU.

Yes, I want to leave my little flower on your grave, mommy, because you didn't want me to be fucked. You loved me and your love wasn't a fuck – no – it wasn't a fucking fuck. Mommy – what have you left behind for me???/??????

in-out-in-out-in-out
that's my body – in-out!!

Punish me – yes – that's all you can do – punish me – just don't love me – it might kill you. I want to blow bubbles – but what's the point?? Down – down – down – push it – down my body. No – I don't have a body – I don't have a body (I just have a mouth and a vagina to be fucked). Come – come – come – into me.

I am no longer

Free willie – all willies should be freed – liberated from their oppression – yes – what's all this feminist shit – we can't help it our willies need to be free.

Life continues – maybe I'll learn to love a woman? Yes – that's a good idea – no willies.

Crush me – kill me – rape me in-out-in-out –
After all – it's only a child.

The picture in Figure 9 was included on the third page of the letter.

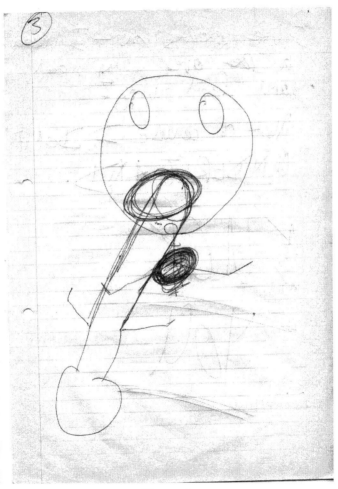

Figure 9
Picture in letter

I tried three times to type this transcript, and it took nearly two weeks to get it finished. The first time that I tried it was late at night and I felt alright until I got to the first "in-out-in-out". I started crying intensely, my tears initially flowing like a waterfall down my cheeks. I couldn't see the keyboard, so I stopped trying to type, and allowed my tears to flow. After weeping for a very short while, I started to feel like I was "floating away". I could not calm myself using my breathing, and this then triggered anxiety. I suddenly felt scared that I was "going away" – so far away that I would never return to myself. At that point, I stood up and walked to the kitchen and somehow managed to make myself a cup of tea. In the step-by-step process of doing this, my tears and my anxiety subsided, as I had to focus all of my energy on this simple task. I sat down with my tea and, as I regained a sense of coming back to myself, I felt calmer. While I experienced the feeling of relative calm and centredness, I allowed my tears to flow again. It felt like I cried for an eternity, although in reality it was probably only for the few minutes it took for me to finish my salty cup of tea. I remember picking up a book titled *Bidpad* (Prayer path) beside my bed just before trying to get to sleep. I asked my guardian angel to guide me to the page I needed to read. I opened the book on a page starting a new chapter – "Insigte van bo" (Insights from above) – the message of that chapter was to surrender all to God when you are at breaking point.

The second time I tried to continue typing this transcript, it was early in the morning. I sat down in my chair at my computer desk and started opening up my computer. Before I had even finished opening it up, I felt like I was just "shutting down". (I had a strong sense that I just had to close myself off from what I was preparing to write about.) I closed my half-open computer and took myself straight to bed, where I stayed until lunch time. I suddenly felt an old, familiar, deep dark depression threatening to trap me again and hold me in its claws of death. I dragged myself out of bed at lunch time and somehow found the strength to start doing a few things that needed to be done, even though I was in a numbed state, devoid of any feeling. As I plodded through my tasks, I slowly started to feel like I was breathing some life-giving oxygen again as I ticked off the boxes on my to-do list for the day. Over the next few days, the depression lifted, and I decided that I was not going to even think about when I would continue writing the chapter. Instead, I was going to meditate every morning until I felt like I was ready to write again, regardless of how long this took. During my meditations, I felt strongly drawn to the colour turquoise. I found the one and only turquoise stone necklace I had and wore it every day. I later researched this a little and realised that this is a colour used for grounding – I needed to ground myself by breathing throughout my writing.

About a week and a half later, having had quite a few meditations, I finally decided to try again. I wept my way through the rest of the transcript, but I stopped to breathe regularly (not just when I felt overwhelmed). Somehow, I finally managed to complete it, and here I am now, feeling my calmness returning to me once more. Thank you to my guardian angel who always promised to catch me when I fall.

When I first read the letter, after finding it in my file, I shook with shock. Initially I engaged in a battle with my mind – I could not specifically recall writing the letter. However, the handwriting was most definitely mine, so I must have written it. I asked myself, "How come I don't remember writing something as shocking as this?" Initially there was no other emotion. As I walked down the passageway, having just read the letter, I experienced the old familiar feeling of watching my feet and wondering whether they were mine and whether they were attached to me or not. After a short talk with Richard, my husband, I cried with a greater sense of relief than grief, although I couldn't quite explain it at the time. Later, I started to realise that I had received the answer I had asked for – there was no longer any doubt in my mind as to who had been responsible for my sexual abuse. A new phase in my healing journey had begun.

READER'S REFLECTION:

Have you ever found yourself desperately searching for an answer to a seemingly unresolvable situation in your life? When you have already tried everything that is within your own control to find the solution but have been unsuccessful, have you ever considered asking for divine intervention to show you an answer that will bring you the peace of mind that you need? I encourage you to just ask, in whatever way feels right for you – it may be prayer, meditation, reading the bible, or even a creative activity that opens you to divine help. Try not to have any expectations on exactly how or when the answer will be given to you – just ask and then let it go, knowing and trusting that you don't need to worry about it anymore.

17

SECOND ST. RAPHAEL'S SANCTUARY HEALING RETREAT – JULY 2016

Hazel

A year after the first healing retreat, I attended my second healing retreat at St Raphael's Sanctuary. It took place only a few months after I had found the letter that I had written to my father more than twenty years ago. Reflecting on it now, I can see that this was a pivotal point in my healing journey. The progress I had made became clearly evident in my paintings, my forgiveness letters and finally, and most significantly, in my projective imagery letter.

Please join me, once again, on a journey through the most significant healing experiences in my second healing retreat.

PAINTING:

Figure 10
"Contained" – Painting at second St. Raphael's Retreat

While my memory of producing this painting is not as vivid as my memory of producing the first painting, what I do recall is that, from the start, my anxiety levels were not as high as they had been during the first painting session. I was more easily able to pick up the paintbrush and allow my hands to choose a colour, and I was able to flow into the experience much more freely. Something in me was unblocking itself through the movement of my hands while painting, and as I slowly started to allow this to happen, my painting emerged before me. (See Figure 10.)

LEFT- AND RIGHT-HANDED JOURNALING TECHNIQUE:

I recall being free from anxiety, feeling calm, and flowing easily into writing my answers while doing this journaling activity. I will now take you through my questions and answers.

Q: What are you trying to tell me?
A: I am able to contain my own darkness and pain.

One of the most difficult challenges for me throughout my healing journey, with so many different therapists at different times in my life, has been the concern that if I truly confronted my fears I would become completely overwhelmed and would no longer be able to keep a foothold in my present life with all its responsibilities. My greatest fear was that I would have a complete breakdown and end up in a psychiatric hospital. I was afraid that I would lose my income and no longer be able to be there for my child. I feared that my husband would not be able to cope, and that our family would be torn apart. At the heart of this lay another fear – the fear that if I broke down completely, I would never be able to be repaired; I wouldn't be able to put the broken pieces of myself back together again and become fully functional. This was an ongoing battle between my head and my heart, as my knowledge of psychology and the nature of the healing process told me that true healing becomes possible through brokenness. Louie Giglio said, "Brokenness is the bow from which God launches the arrow of healing". However, theoretical knowledge only sinks to the level of the heart through personal life experience.

Q: Anything else?
A: I am able to contain others' pain.

Q: What is the red and black?
A: Aggression, violence, pain, trauma.

Q: **And the blue?**

A: Moving what is able to contain to becoming what is able to heal. What contains, heals. Moving into and through the darkness. The container becomes the healer.

Here I find the resolution to this battle in accessing my soul – that part of myself that is able to contain my pain while simultaneously healing me by moving directly into and then through my pain. Accessing my soul would finally allow me to release my pain and to then move on towards being able to heal others.

Q: **The violet and the lilac?**

A: Spiritual wisdom, a source of protection, a strength beyond words, an eternal source of refuge. What enables the light to penetrate the darkness within.

Here I am reminded of how violet and lilac have been a theme in my healing for more than twenty years. I had written the word "Wisdom" in purple paint on the inside of my "Who I am" painted box during the first St Raphael's workshop. Also, the mandala I painted during the second retreat contained a violet wheel in the centre, with violet feathers emanating from the wheel, and a violet border. (See Figure 11.)

Figure 11
Mandala painting – Second St. Raphael's Retreat

Furthermore, a clairvoyant I saw many years ago had told me that the strong purple light that I feel attracted to is the "light" side of the "dark" vicious snake. Most significantly, all the feathers on my drawings of my guardian angel are violet. According to Pauline Willis, a colour reflexologist, violet is the colour of the crown chakra and, as such, is the colour most closely related to spirituality, insight, the higher self and divine wisdom. It is also the place where our lower and higher selves can become united (Pauline Wills, 2002).

While the theme of trauma is clearly evident in the paintings from both the first retreat and the second retreat (seen in the use of red and black), the second painting is open, while the first one was closed (behind the diagonal black lines). This evidences the shift from my trauma initially being emotionally inaccessible, towards me opening myself up to experiencing my own immense pain related to the trauma. Furthermore, my journaling now indicates not only my own ability to heal myself, but also my emerging ability to heal others. My healing progress is further evident in my experiences of the painting and journaling activities

– a shift towards flowing into my own answers and a release from the anxiety that was blocking my answers.

FORGIVENESS LETTER THREE:

For this exercise, I wrote a letter to myself, from my guardian angel. The letter is presented below.

Dear Hazel

The purpose of this trauma is to enable you to reach out and heal others on the same journey as you – to carry them through the trauma, towards their light. The start of this healing begins with writing your experience. Reconnecting with your pain, at times, will be difficult, but your tears will flow with your writing, through your writing, towards the end of the story. This is where the closure in your story will give you wings to carry others on their journeys too.

CREATE AS MUCH SPACE AS POSSIBLE IN YOUR LIFE NOW FOR YOUR WRITING.

This is both the completion of your own healing as well as the start of your healing of others.

Trust in your own strength to allow your writing to move you finally through, and then beyond the trauma of your own pain.

TRUST ME, LOVE ME, LET YOURSELF BE HELD WHEN THE PAIN RETURNS, THEN YOU WILL HOLD OTHERS.

Remain focused and at peace, I am with you always.

Your Angel.

While reading through this letter now, I am amazed at how so much of its contents reflect my current experience of writing this book and my experience of my guardian angel.

There are certain parts of the letter that I find particularly meaningful. They include the following:

"... Your tears will flow with your writing, through your writing ..."

I cannot count the number of times that I have called Louise while writing, feeling emotionally overwhelmed, and she has somehow carried me through, enabling me to continue writing. More recently, I have noticed my own progress in sometimes being able to carry myself through my tears on my own, by simply continuing to write and perhaps expressing my current emotion in my writing.

"This is where the closure of your story will give you wings to carry others on their journeys too."

I have experienced many frustrations with wanting to create more time to commit to moving forward with my work and income. However, this sentence reminds me that completing the writing of this book is a necessary part of my own healing, which needs to find further closure before I can move on to healing others.

"Remain focused and at peace, I am with you always," signed *"Your Angel".*

My guardian angel appears in most of my very old drawings, some of which express trauma. There has always been a part of me that is aware of her presence in my life but, at times, I have forgotten this. However, I have always been able to reconnect with her in times of crisis, although I often need to remind myself to do so.

Looking back once again, it is now powerfully healing for me to reflect on my own healing progress through these letters of forgiveness. Only a year before I wrote this letter, I had been immersed in so much rage, pain and anxiety that I had been unable to even consider attempting to try to find any purpose in it. Now I was starting to find some peace as well as a clear, new sense of direction and life purpose. Over a period of twelve months, a transformation had taken place.

PROJECTIVE IMAGERY LETTER:

As with my "Broken Child" individual therapy session, we were asked to select one photo from a spread of photos without thinking. We were then asked to write a letter to our adult self as if we are the object in the photo. The purpose of this was to reconnect with our higher self, which provides access to divine wisdom / God. The content of the writing is the voice of God / the higher, wise self. The picture that I selected (Figure 12), together with the content of the letter, is presented below.

Figure 12
"Take these broken wings and learn to fly again"
(Lyrics from the Richard Page song, "Broken Wings")

Dear Hazel

Your wings are opening up through pain, they are spreading across your sky, you are gaining perspective from a place where all can be seen, your vision is clear, vital, highly focused and more in tune with your strength than your brokenness. Your wings glide effortlessly through space, there is little resistance, yet your altitude is maintained – maintaining your ability to see what it is you need to find, with spectacular panoramic views below, above and all around.

∞

In your wings others will be sheltered, rested, protected, and then slowly you will lift them towards the skies as you take flight together, supporting and guiding them and then finally watching them spread their wings and take to their own flight, directing themselves, migrating to new skies.

∞

You are immeasurably strong and will always have the strength that will enable others to replenish their own depleted reserves.

∞

You will land when, and where you need to, to renew your own strength, but not for too long as you now know that you were born to fly, and your flight will be far further than you have been carried through your own pain, in your own brokenness.

∞

You are almost ready to take to flight, very soon now you will fly. Your first mother taught you how to fly, you have always known how to, just broke your wings through pain. She is now with you again, the wind beneath your wings.

You will soar high and she will be there to watch you take to the skies once again.

You are an eagle now my child, my eagle.

Love yours in flight

Several parts of this letter stand out for me as I read it again:

"You are gaining perspective from a place where all can be seen"

As I reflect on this now, I realise its significance – this is the place of my soul.

"In your wings others will be sheltered, rested, protected and then slowly you will lift them towards the skies ... supporting them and guiding them ... directing themselves, migrating to new skies."

Again, as in the forgiveness letter, this expresses how my soul knows that I will move forward towards healing others and empowering them too to re-align with their True Self and to live their own true purpose.

"You now know that you were born to fly, and your flight will be far further than you have been carried through your own pain, in your own brokenness."

Here, I have the answer to my greatest fear. I am able to put my broken pieces back together in a new form without permanently losing my foothold in the responsibilities of my current life. Furthermore, I can now see that there is a beautiful cyclical process at work in which I am moving towards becoming a wounded healer.

"Your first mother taught you to fly, you have always known how to, just broke your wings through pain. She is now with you again, the wind beneath your wings."

Here I can see the clear synchronicity with my healing dreams of flying and specifically the dream in which I told my brother, "I have always known how to fly". I recall that, while journaling one morning on the retreat, I cried intensely as I expressed my intuition that I needed to meditate and reconnect with my foster mother each time I continued writing this book. Her spirit would be with me and would be flowing through me as I wrote. Some of the words I wrote in my journal that day are: "Through me, my spirit in you, this will become possible. This is why you are here; this is why this has happened to you." As I write about it now, my tears are flowing in this beautiful moment of peace and relief, as she is the guiding energy through my hands while I write. I want to thank her once again for laying the early foundation of love in my life. I lost her, but we are now reunited through my writing.

Reading through this letter again, I feel my tears welling up and, as a few stream down my face, I realise that they are tears of enormous relief; a sense that my brokenness is finally healing and that I am finding its purpose in my life.

My memory of writing this projective imagery letter is still crystal clear. My writing flowed like a river moving naturally along the path of least resistance. While I drew the infinity sign, it felt like a natural pause, completely free from anxiety and stress, before I moved spontaneously onto the next paragraph. I experienced a sense of peaceful detachment, almost as if someone else was holding the pen and doing the writing for me. When I signed the letter, *"Yours in flight"*, I experienced an immensely powerful sense of peace, leaving me with a deep knowing that I was never alone; I always had my guardian angel with me.

I would like to share with you how the symbol of the eagle has returned to me in a synchronistic way since writing this letter. There have been a few occasions when I have felt emotionally overwhelmed by either my personal pain or a sense that I would not be able to create the time and space in my life to fulfil my dream of writing this book. Many obstacles have been placed in my path and at times I have become disillusioned and angry with God and the universe for not making it easier for me to reach my dream. On a few of these occasions, I noticed an eagle flying above me while I was driving along our farm road. On one occasion, the eagle was perched on a nearby fence post at the side of the road. I stopped my car and examined it closely for quite some time – it was as still as a statue. When I finally started driving again, it flew closely alongside my car for a short distance before flying away! In another incident, after I had experienced another challenging year, I opened a Christmas present from a friend who knew nothing about the symbol of the eagle from my retreat. The present was a statue of an eagle flying, and in her card, my friend asked me to read what was written underneath the stand of the statue. It read: "He will cover you with his feathers, and under his wings you will find refuge. His faithfulness will be your shield and rampart" (Psalm 91:4). I later noticed that the eagle had one foot broken off – a reminder to me that it is only through my brokenness that I will learn to fly. It was a second-hand statue with a hugely significant meaning – I had become a second-hand statue of an eagle in one of Louise's psychodrama activities on this healing retreat, because I was broken and had forgotten how to fly!

The previous year (after the first healing retreat), I had done the projective imagery letter writing activity as "The Broken Child". The letter I wrote for this activity on the second healing retreat clearly shows how I had moved into, and then through my own brokenness, moving beyond it towards healing others.

In conclusion, I see that a beautiful tapestry of my transformational healing journey has emerged through my paintings, letters of forgiveness and projective imagery letters. This tapestry has been woven by hand through different forms of writing and painting, and these activities have been the tools that started to create a truly beautiful design. Through the use of each technique, my healing progress has become clearly evident over time, and there have also been many synchronicities with these responses in my life. This is evidence of my soul expressing the same message through a variety of channels and guiding me towards healing. I now also know that it is only through a greater, divine intervention that this design has been made possible.

I hope that you have enjoyed your walk with me through the second part of my retreat journey. As you have become aware of the immense progress in my own healing through these two retreats, may you too allow this awareness to lead you towards finding solace and faith in your own ability to heal from your pain.

18

SECOND CHANCE: ST. RAPHAEL'S SANCTUARY HEALING RETREAT

Louise

This will be a short chapter, as I have already explained the psycho-spiritual nature of the St Raphael's Sanctuary Healing Retreat and the themes covered in the retreat. The main aim is to bring people in touch with God and their True Self. We believe that no true and lasting healing can take place without God, as He is the Great Healer. This is a fact that has been brought home even more throughout my journey with Hazel.

As I have mentioned previously, Hazel attended a second St Raphael's Sanctuary retreat a year after the first one, and the changes in her were remarkable. When you see someone weekly, you don't always see the changes that others, who are not in contact with that person as often, will attest to. I think this is what happened to us – I had not noticed the extent of the changes in Hazel. Yet, comparing Hazel's first experience of the healing retreat with the second one, the extent of the growth, healing, and increase in wisdom was mind-blowing. I won't give a detailed description of all the activities and insights I witnessed during

Hazel's attendance at the second retreat, but I would like to mention that some activities were still challenging for Hazel. It was not as if everything were suddenly a walk in the park. Ironically, the picture she painted during the first creative activity on the second retreat was strikingly similar to the first painting on the first retreat: both contained red, black and yellow stripes and splotches. Yet, on the second retreat she could remain present for the uncomfortable questions, complete the activities despite her anxiety levels, and explore her own thoughts and beliefs in more depth. The themes that arose during the second retreat were also different. Her foster mother, in whose care she had been placed for the first eighteen months of her life, was a prominent theme on the second retreat. Hazel's foster home was a place of love and acceptance, and the majority of the messages from her True Self were encouraging her to not just look at the "bad" times of her life, but to also remember the "good" times, and to draw strength from these. The three most moving moments for me from Hazel's second healing retreat epitomise how far she had come in her healing journey.

The first thing I recall is that during the group "How I came to be here", the participants were asked to break into pairs and to explain their life graph. As providence would have it, Hazel and I were paired up for this activity. We could have said, "We already know each other's stories, so let's chat about something else," but we didn't. I remember how Hazel explained her life story, embracing all aspects of it: the good, the bad, the ugly and the beautiful. However, the thing that moved me most was that when I explained my life story, I was deeply struck by God's Grace in my life. Hazel's life story could have been mine: I could have been born into her family. I wasn't more deserving than she was; I didn't do anything better than she did. It was only through God's Grace that my life story was different from hers. Of course, this opens up a whole lot of questions about our lives, the purpose of our lives and the reasons why our life stories read the way they do. Surely it is not due to a coincidence. There is a saying we use at St Raphael's Sanctuary that goes, "Our wounds become

153

our redemption" or, as Jason Gray sings in his song "Glow in the dark" about how our wounds are where God's light and love shines through, "The more broke you are, the more the light gets through". If we would only realise this, it would change our disastrous past into God's love story for each of us.

Through this insight, I was able to experience on a soul level (not just on the level of my mind) that we are all spiritual beings having a human experience. This truth humbled me to realise that my soul is in no way superior to anyone else's. When accompanying someone on their healing journey, there is no place for my ego, or for the thoughts and beliefs of my false self. I don't have to fix anyone. Every person already possesses all the wisdom they need to be healed. They have just forgotten to listen to their soul, a conduit of God's voice. My role as a healer, with a small "h", is to provide opportunities for them to re-discover that truth for themselves; to be an instrument of healing in God's hands so that He can reach the other person through me. As St Teresa of Avila said,

> "God has no body now on earth but yours,
> No hands but yours, No feet but yours,
> Yours are the eyes through which he is to look out
> God's compassion to the world;
> Yours are the feet with which he is to go about doing good;
> Yours are the hands with which he is to bless men now."

For that to happen, I need to empty myself and take my ego out of the way, to align my will with God's will. Sometimes the most important task is for me to reflect God's love and acceptance to that person in their most difficult time, so that they know that they are not alone; that they are loved.

The second thing I recall from the second retreat is the projective imagery letter that Hazel wrote about the eagle flying. I can still see, in my mind's eye, where Hazel sat on that cold winter's morning. I remember the almost-giddy feeling I experienced as she read about flying. An incredible feeling washed over me; a feeling as of someone who had walked a long journey and caught sight of the end for the first time. It was a beautiful sight! Flying: free, unencumbered, not weighed down. The focus was on the future, despite everything Hazel had experienced in her past. Hazel had shifted from being trapped in her past for almost forty years to embracing a future of flying; a future with positive possibilities. This was indeed a major breakthrough; this was a sacred moment.

The third thing I remember is the last session of the retreat, when we were already winding down and tying up the last loose ends. I remember Hazel alluding to her past as she was giving feedback to the group. Up until that stage, Hazel had never shared publicly that she had been sexually abused. I extended an invitation for her to elaborate to the group if she felt comfortable enough. I reiterated that it was her choice. To my absolute amazement, she took up the offer and shared aspects of her past with the group. There is something about sharing our wounds aloud. I'm not sure what it is. Perhaps it is the last bit of denial that we trump through speaking up, or our willingness to shatter others' perspectives of us and to stand unmasked and naked before them. That is the ultimate step to self-acceptance. It is possibly one of the biggest risks that we can take. At the right time and in the right place with the right people, our risk-taking is more often than not rewarded with love and acceptance. In the process, we are liberated to be real and unmasked, with all our ugly or shameful bits revealed, and to be accepted in spite of them. Through that, we are indeed released to soar.

READER'S REFLECTION:

Reflect on your wounds. Embrace them even if you have no idea of how they will be your redemption. For now, just embrace them and be grateful for them.

Let's end this chapter with a challenge: Take a risk to reveal to someone some of your ugly or shameful bits. Unmask yourself. Our wish for you is to be liberated; to soar.

19
JOSHUA: THE LEADER OF OUR JOURNEY INTO THE PROMISED LAND

Hazel

Figure 13
"It is no secret what God can do" (Jim Reeves)

After two years on the devastating emotional roller-coaster of hope and despair, through two miscarriages and ongoing failed infertility treatments, we adopted Joshua. He was the answer to the words, "Thy will be done" that I had scribbled onto a piece of paper and put into my pocket on our final IVF attempt in 2012. In looking back, we have since come to realise that Joshua was probably conceived around the same time that we received the news that our final IVF attempt had failed. After three fertilised eggs had been implanted into my womb, I had been convinced that we would at last be successful. Little did I know, when we received the news that not one of them had attached, that my new journey towards healing had only just begun. My journey together with Joshua was to be one that would embrace deep sexual healing for both of us, at a level far beyond the mind and guided by the same divine source that had brought us together in a synchronistic way.

My husband and I finally thought we had it all mapped out perfectly when we found Joshua a place at a full-time preschool about half an hour's drive away. It had a very good reputation and was a feeder preschool for an equally reputable primary school. We were incredibly relieved, after having struggled with childcare problems for nearly three years, with both of us working. We were certain that the exhaustion that came with the twelve-hour days would be worthwhile in the long term, offering Joshua continuity of care at last.

Life's maps very seldom navigate us to our initial intended destination. Approximately six months later, we started to lose Joshua who, for some unknown reason, became consumed with rage that manifested as ongoing, immensely aggressive, destructive behaviour. At the same time, we started to notice some hypersexual behaviour. For example, he would strongly insist on accompanying his friends whenever any one of them went to the toilet. When we insisted that he wait for his turn, he would resist strongly, despite it becoming clear that he didn't need to go himself, as he would then go off and play when his friend returned. He also suddenly regressed with his potty training after having maintained good control for a few months. We started to become very concerned after we received a phone call from his preschool manager regarding his problematic sexual behaviour. We spoke to Joshua about "good and bad touch" and only received denials when we questioned him about what the teachers had told us about his sexual behaviour at preschool.

One day, while we were in the noisy, chaotic state clinic, I noticed Joshua unexpectedly turn his head in towards Richard's chest, with tears streaming down his face. Soon afterwards, while he was running around again on his Eveready batteries as usual, Richard came to tell me that he had asked Joshua whether any-one had ever touched him on his private parts in a way that he didn't want them to. Joshua's mood had suddenly changed from his usual, hyperactive, happy self to one of crying and pleading with Richard not to tell me. He had told Richard that his best friend at preschool had done this to him and had said, "Don't tell." Joshua had then gone on to tell Richard that he must not tell me, as this was to be a secret between only him and Daddy. I suddenly felt as if time was standing still and my world went into slow motion while Richard shared this with me. There was still a part of me that thought it could not be true. Yet, a bigger part of me knew that it must be true, as I myself had noticed Joshua's sudden and intense change in mood and his increased tearfulness. I didn't want to believe what I was hearing and yet, somehow, so many questions had just been answered. Shock sank in as I tried to breathe deeply into my numbness and to try and see, through a thick fog, what I needed to do next to heal our son.

The journey ahead, although daunting, now at least held a seed of hope for healing. We were referred to a highly recommended play therapist with specialist experience in the field of sexual abuse. She was an hour and a half's drive away, but we believed she was the best person to heal Joshua. We were prepared to move heaven and earth for his healing. My brother had been sexually abused in his youth, and I so desperately wanted to save our son from the long-term damage that my brother had had to carry with him into his adulthood before his healing journey could begin. After our first interview with the play therapist, Joshua was suspended from preschool, leaving us not only emotionally devastated but also really struggling to cope. With us both working, it placed a great strain on our finances and on our marriage.

While I hugged the play therapist after Joshua's first therapy session, I was in tears when she said to me, "His healing will be your healing." She was living her words to me; not merely speaking them. I somehow felt her tremendously strong faith within myself, and the ground beneath me felt more stable. However, the deeper significance of her words to me was yet to be revealed. My sense that I would heal from the pain I felt for Joshua, as his mother, started to transform into an awareness that the pain I felt for him was also a reflection of my own sexual wounds.

Joshua spent a month at home with us, and after four sessions of play therapy, his rage and hypersexual behaviour had improved significantly, and we felt that we had begun to find our angel again. After a few months of him being cared for at home by a friend of mine, we found him a mornings-only local Montessori preschool that we thought was suitable for him, as it had only a small number of children and had a wonderful teacher who was exceptionally understanding of his problems. Our working lives were thrown into chaos again as we worked around his mornings-only, term-time-only preschool hours. After many unsuccessful attempts at finding after-school care, I was guilt-ridden and at my wits' end, and I was considering giving up my work as a therapy assistant at the old age home, which I not only loved, but also needed financially. After a term, just when we were starting to regain our footing and Joshua seemed to be happy at his new preschool, he was asked to leave. There had been another sexual incident resulting in the other child's parents not wanting Joshua to attend any longer.

I hit my lowest point. My mind, body and soul came to a dead end and I fell into a deep depression, only putting one foot in front of the other with the help of antidepressants. Our heartache and pain continued on a roller-coaster of hope and devastation similar to the one we had experienced on our journey towards adopting Joshua. He immediately started attending play therapy again but, just as we believed we were seeing signs of further healing in his play therapy, there was another incident in which he acted out in a sexually inappropriate way with a friend at home. While I knew that healing is a circular process, rather than a linear one, I still struggled immensely with this when it came to his healing process. Surely my son should be fully healed by now! After another few months with no signs of any further problematic sexual behaviour, we started regaining a sense of hope and decided to tread carefully and place him back into the Montessori preschool one morning a week. However, two weeks later, there was yet another sexual incident, this time between Joshua and my brother's girlfriend's son, who is about a year younger than Joshua, while we were having a family braai. Now it had gone too far – it had started to move into my direct family and put a strain on my very close relationship with my brother. About a month after that, we had to cancel our tenth wedding anniversary weekend away, as my brother's psychiatrist strongly recommended that Joshua not be allowed to play with my brother's girlfriend's son, due to the relatively recent sexual incident between the two of them. The plan had been for Joshua to be looked after by my brother and his girlfriend, who would closely supervise his play. However, due to the repetitive nature of Joshua's sexual acting-out, it was considered to be too risky, and Joshua had to be told that he was not allowed to play with this friend of his because of what had happened. Once again, I took Joshua back to play therapy, but this time Edith, the play therapist, referred him to our family doctor, realising that he needed further professional intervention and possibly the help of a psychiatrist. Having got a referral from the doctor to a clinical psychologist, I had another session with Edith during which we discussed my own childhood in more depth. She felt that she had possibly found a missing link, and she referred us on to an attachment specialist. Although this made sense to me at the time, when I thought about it again, I was very unsure about whether it was the right route for us to follow. My faith in

Joshua's healing was wearing very thin and it was leaving me in an emotional desert – completely barren, with no sign of a path to guide my direction. I felt depressed and helpless, and I was descending into despair and severe emotional dehydration, with no oasis in sight. I also felt guilty about questioning whether or not to follow Edith's referral at that stage. Who was I to complain about having no direction to guide me when I had been given a route to follow but was choosing not to follow it immediately?

With tears streaming from my eyes, having just had to postpone our wedding anniversary weekend away at the last minute, and already being emotionally exhausted, with no sign of another break in sight, I parked my car outside my place of work. I paused and breathed, only for more tears to flow. I realised that I was in no state of mind to work, so I contacted Louise, who was once again there for me to pour out my heart to.

As I drove up the 3 km pot-holed farm road in my beat-up old car on the way to Louise's house, I tried to clear the thick layer of dust from the front windscreen, using the windscreen wipers. Like my tearful eyes, they only seemed to leave more stains on the windows before the dust was blown back up again, further obscuring my vision of the path ahead through dust and tears. As I began to lose myself again in my pain, I became blinded to my journey, losing perspective on anything but my destination – my desperation for Joshua to heal within my own self-imposed time frame. He was scheduled to start school in just over a year's time, and he needed to be fully healed before then.

I allowed my tears to flow as I shared my pain and turmoil about the seemingly endless period of play therapy, financial and marital strain, and preschool suspensions. I had developed tunnel vision over the previous year, in my desperate pursuit of healing for our son, and I could still see no light at the end of the tunnel. In my mind, body and soul, I seemed to have lost not only my strength to carry on, but also my sense of which way was forward. How could I move forward when I didn't know which way I was facing anymore? We discussed the option of simply, for the moment, not pursuing any further professional intervention for Joshua, but rather exploring everyday things like the "Nanny" programme on television and just letting time show us a sign before we made any further decisions. Louise asked me what it was that I really wanted to do for myself at that time. There was a very long silence that persisted as I struggled to see what I had started to become blind to – my sense of self and my personal dreams. As I searched the dark recesses of my soul, I finally grasped the switch for my fog lights and turned them on. The visibility of the path ahead briefly returned to me as I softly muttered that I wanted to write my book and move towards my play therapy induction training. We talked about the steps I would need to take to reconnect with my own path towards my personal dreams, despite Joshua's problems. First and foremost, I needed to re-frame my perception of his problems and accept that his healing might take a lot longer than I had hoped. Although this still felt devastating, the renewed perspective enabled me to look towards different long-term options and ways of learning to live with his problems and manage his problems, without losing hope for the future. (One of these was the option of homeschooling.) Furthermore, I needed to set some small short-term goals towards committing to writing my book while I waited for further news on my internship training.

As I drove back to a restaurant in the town to gather my strength before returning to work, I was acutely aware that chronological time still seemed to be standing still on the battlefield of Joshua's healing. However, very gradually, a whole new perspective on time's healing power slowly became visible through the eyes of my soul. Each letter in the word "re-frame" seemed to be forming a shoot, emerging from a tiny seed, as it started to take root in the dry, arid ground beneath me. I needed to accept where Joshua was at with respect to his healing progress, and I needed to surrender to living with the unanswered question of "What next?"

As my latte coffee warmed me on the inside, my focus slowly started to shift away from the turmoil in my head and heart, towards my immediate senses. I felt the slight vibrations on the wooden floor as the waitress approached me, and I noticed the passing cars outside on the street as my hands warmed around my coffee mug. While I took one slow sip at a time, I started to become aware of how the warmth of the log fire seemed to be taking root inside me as I started to relax, with a sense of warmth approaching my being. As my mind started to become more centred in my immediate surroundings, I heard the words of a song with crystalline clarity, "It is no secret what God can do." The words and tune repeatedly played to me as I shifted from hearing them, to singing along with them, to becoming a channel through which they flowed from the centre of my soul. I could not let go of the song.

Although I could not connect the song to a specific memory at that time, a few days later, quite unexpectedly, I noticed a Jim Reeves CD in our local shop, on special no less. On picking it up, I realised that it contained the song I had heard in the restaurant. The Jim Reeves record my parents had had when I was a child had this same song on it, which had now traced me after thirty years. I intuitively knew that I needed to purchase the CD.

While listening to the song on the CD, I started to feel a vague sense of relief; somehow there was a sense of space expanding around me in a bubble of peace. Suspended in this bubble were all the unanswered questions regarding Joshua's healing which, despite being beyond my personal control, I could now reach out and touch without bursting the bubble. The song revealed to me the answer to the question of "What next?" regarding his healing. For the moment, I needed to surrender his healing to a higher, divine source of healing that would carry him. At the same time, I had to be still within myself. Wow ... that was a tall order and certainly not the answer that I had been looking for! However, on another level it made sense – we had done all within our personal control to enable Joshua's healing process. Ironically, we now needed to let go of that control and simply trust that, when the time was right, we would be shown a clear sign as to what the next step would be for him.

Guilt continued to threaten to overwhelm me, as I was a mother who had not succeeded in healing her son and had not followed up on the last referral. The battle between my mind and my soul felt never-ending. However, I slowly started to become aware that the bubble of peace continued expanding, creating more space for my soul's voice to be heard in the midst of the battle, thanks to the gift of Jim Reeves's music. His words in the song became the language of my soul.

Despite my grave fears, I decided to meet with Joshua's pre-school teacher again to discuss any possibility of his returning to preschool. I left with a bit of a heavy heart after we had agreed that I would contact her again once we had followed up on his referral to a psychiatrist via the doctor. She also recommended that I contact the dominee (pastor) of the NGK (Dutch-Reformed Church) for spiritual healing.

As life continued on its busy roller-coaster ride, I got to speaking to a friend about Joshua. My friend told me that the dominee of her church might know of someone who could offer Joshua spiritual healing, if I chose to try this option. I did not give it much more thought, but one morning, while driving to work past this dominee's house, I asked to be shown a sign if I was to follow this route. Within less than fifteen minutes, while I was on my way in to work, I walked directly past the dominee at the Old Age Home where I worked! Only on second thought did I have a sense that I needed to say more than just "Good morning" to him, and I arranged to meet with him at lunchtime. We spent an hour together talking about and praying for Joshua. The dominee then referred me on to another dominee who had specialised in spiritual healing. As I walked back to work, the battle between mind and soul intensified and became manifest in the copy of the Christian Bible he had given me, which I held in my hands. My mind was telling me that if I was to explore spiritual healing for our son, it would be through an alternative Eastern approach, which is almost the exact opposite of the NGK approach! However, my soul kept telling me to follow the signs I was being given, regardless of the exact direction that they were pointing me towards. As I placed the Bible into my locker at work, despite thinking that it might somehow explode on impact, I briefly returned to a sense of peace within myself.

While driving to the dominee's house a few weeks later, the by-now-too-familiar struggle between a sense of hope and one of despair started to return to me. It was by no means overwhelming, but it was rather more like listening to a stuck record (not a Jim Reeves one!). I felt a lot more at ease now, being able to listen to the record, rather than becoming the music it was playing. Despite this, I had a clear expectation of bringing Joshua back with me the next time, for his first spiritual healing session through the NGK. Surely, I would not have been shown such a clear sign if this was not to be the outcome. However, life only ever reveals its pathway through the twist in the tale – a twist that is only ever visible retrospectively.

Having shared Joshua's story with the dominee, I listened intently to the dominee's descriptions of his experiences of healing others who he believed were "possessed by demons". His healing ability seemed to be transferred to me, manifesting itself on a physical level as an intense pins-and-needles sensation in my hands and arms while he prayed for Joshua. I will never forget the healing energy I felt at that moment. I was given guidance with a prayer to use myself while laying hands on Joshua once he was asleep. This prayer focused on praying for his release from the spirits of rejection, fear of rejection, lust and inter-generational curse. I was left with two certainties in my mind: firstly, that the dominee clearly was a genuinely deeply gifted spiritual healer and, secondly, that the perspective and framework from which he was working conflicted deeply with my own on many levels (e.g. he was of the opinion that all Sangomas were possessed by demons). Could I marry these two certainties together? Despite his different perspective, my heart hit the floor when he told me that he did not work directly with young children, as he felt that he would be encroaching on the parents' territory of authority, and hence gave specific spiritual guidance to parents on healing their young children themselves. With a bit of a heavy heart,

I thanked him for his time and advice, and set off on the road again ... a road of initial frustration, confusion and uncertainty that took me to a restaurant for lunch.

Over lunch, while Googling a book he had referred me to (*Defeating Dark Angels* by Charles Kraft), I became more certain of the different perspectives that we were coming from, and I felt my frustration, uncertainty and anxiety begin to raise their heads again. However, while driving home, I switched on the Jim Reeves CD again and tried to surrender to the music. The song "Have thine own way, Lord" spoke to me as I attempted to grasp the essence of its message for me at that point in time. Despite my internal battle, the bubble of peace began to expand further. Gradually, I started to experience a sense of knowing that I needed to follow the sign and that I would be the person to heal Joshua, in more ways than I had originally perceived possible. I would be able to marry the two different theoretical perspectives and frameworks – they did not need to be in opposition to the gift of spiritual healing. This gift, in essence, is the ability to become a channel for a higher, universal source of healing, and to transfer this healing to those in need. I needed to embrace becoming that channel of healing for our son, myself.

For quite some time after that, I struggled with following the dominee's advice about the laying on of hands while praying, as I was always so very tired myself by the time that Joshua was asleep, that I found it hard to focus my energy on laying my hands on him at that time. However, the few times that I did lay my hands on him while praying for him, my hands felt as if they were being directed and moved by an energy that was beyond myself, as they were naturally drawn towards being just above his heart. The sensation of pins and needles in my hands was very strong, and it was accompanied by an absolute sense of peace and serenity. Although I felt like I was losing my battle with my own tiredness after he was asleep, I discovered that he relaxed deeply and lay still when I stroked him gently down the middle of his back, so this became the new way forward: the healing power of touch.

I was immensely relieved when Joshua's teacher agreed to have him back at preschool, initially one day a week, after she received the news that we had decided not to pursue the option of seeing a psychiatrist, but had rather decided to follow the route of spiritual healing. A beautiful synchronicity emerged when she shared with me an intensely powerful experience of confrontation with some kind of dark demon in her personal family life. This had confirmed her faith in the power of prayer and spiritual healing, and hence she felt sure that it was the right path, together with firm discipline, boundaries, and love. We had narrowly averted placing Joshua in the local government preschool due to concerns about staffing levels, and we had placed him in the Montessori school instead. Had he been in the government preschool, he might not have been shown the same level of compassion and understanding of his difficulties or have been given a second chance to re-enter after his suspension. This pattern of synchronicities with regard to his schooling began to reveal to me a guidance from a divine higher source – one that was opening doors on his healing journey and offering light in the darkness. As I continued writing this book, we had reached the end of the last term of school. After Joshua had attended about twelve days on a part-time basis, his teacher was very pleased with the significant improvement in his general behaviour and with the absence of any signs of inappropriate sexual behaviour, and she had offered him a full-time place for the following year. I felt myself breathing deeply at that moment, as a part of me still had fears of further repeats of his inappropriate sexual behaviour. However, I was trying to learn to accept and live with this fear and to not let it deprive him of another chance to succeed as his healing journey progressed. We were then able to look forward to a new year with his schooling, although with some trepidation, while not allowing ourselves to be blinded by our fear.

Joshua was the initial signpost pointing me towards the path of my own healing, as he placed my hand on the handle, opening the door to my unconscious sexual trauma. Looking back, the beauty of the synchronicity of our healing journeys together shines through in the timing – I had just begun to find a light at the end of the tunnel of my own immensely traumatic healing, before having to support him through his own sexual abuse. As I write, I am still at a loss for words to describe this pain – words can merely scratch at the surface of it. However, through supporting Joshua, I gained further insight into how victims of sexual abuse can often re-victimise others, unless they have the support and opportunity to find healing. What was heart-wrenchingly painful for me was that it was our angel who, as a victim, was continuing to re-victimise others, despite having had extensive intervention through play therapy. This devastating result led us onto a path of spiritual healing for him. It has been this spiritual path that has been the key to unlocking and releasing pain for both of us at the most critical times in both of our healing journeys. Joshua's re-victimising of others, on such a deeply painful and personal level, became the seed that finally grew into my ability to start to forgive my mother as I pieced together her own childhood history of sexual abuse. Joshua's recurring problem with sexual behaviour only finally started to heal significantly after I had begun to embrace forgiving my mother. I thank him now for bringing me to this place of forgiveness.

Joshua continues every day to heal me through his playfulness, while teaching me to not only befriend, but also to embrace my deepest fears. I have opened up opportunities for his healing through play therapy and, ultimately, through re-accessing my own spiritual healing ability with him. Both of our healing journeys seem to have been woven together through divine providence, leaving me with a sense of absolute faith that we were brought together to enable each other's healing.

I can only hope that my experience, shared with you in this chapter, will serve as a light in the darkness on your own jour-neys with your children as you heal each other. If this does not speak to you, or make sense to you now, just take from it what is helpful. It may make more sense to you at a later stage, or perhaps it never will. Regardless of that, I thank you for reading it and allowing me to share it with you.

20

FINDING PURPOSE
THROUGH PAIN

Hazel

I was once again immensely frustrated and stressed by obstacles being constantly placed in my path towards following
my heart's desire – this time I wanted to attend a volunteers'
meeting at the Child Trauma Clinic where Joshua had been having
play therapy. My husband's car needed repairs before we could
use it for a long journey, and I would have to travel to the meeting by train. This meant that I would miss some of the morning
session, as well as some of the afternoon session (assuming that
the train ran on schedule, which it rarely does!). It also meant
being up at 4 am to get the train for a three-hour journey and a
fourteen-hour day, with all the travelling. Just before I was ready
to tear my hair out, I had a moment of serenity and I asked my
guardian angel whether it could be made possible for me to attend
the full sessions on all three days, if that was what was meant to
be. I then mostly managed to stop worrying about the outcome.
A few days later, I received a message saying that one of the Social
Workers was ill and the volunteers' training had been postponed
for a few days. My husband now had time to repair our car and

169

it meant that I would not miss any time on the training course. I knew somehow that my path had been cleared because I had found the peace of mind to surrender the problem to a higher source. A few weeks prior to that, I had also found out about a two-day training seminar being run by the Child Trauma Clinic on "Children with Problem Sexual Behaviours", which I desperately would have liked to attend, but the cost was impossible for me to meet. When the manager at my workplace handed me the same pamphlet advertising the seminar, I experienced a brief moment of frustration about the lack of finances, but I once again asked my guardian angel to please show me a sign to make it possible for me to attend the seminar. Little did I know, though, of the greater unseen plan that lay ahead for me at the volunteers' meeting – so much more of divine intervention was soon to be revealed to me!

As I started chatting to some of the other volunteers in the reception area before the volunteers' meeting began, I realised that they were all post-graduate students looking towards gaining practical experience in play therapy. When the meeting began, we were all asked to share a little of why we were there and what we hoped to gain from volunteering. Slowly, as the others shared their stories, I started to put the pieces together ... I was on an internship programme with Psychology Honours and Social Work students and a newly graduated psychologist, not merely a group of volunteers from the community! Tears welled up in my eyes as the Social Worker talked about the different aspects of the internship programme, one of which included free attendance at the training seminars in exchange for assisting with setting up, packing up and doing attendance registers. My prayer had been answered – I now had my free ticket to the seminar that I so much wanted to attend.

While we all shared a little of our pasts, our hopes and our expectations, I was quite unexpectedly transported back more than twenty years to the time that I had completed my own studies. Past chapters since then, in both my personal life and my working life, started to flash past me in slow motion, as time stood still. In that still moment, I started to sense a possible reason as to why I had "wasted" all those years in my working life – had I needed to first heal my personal wounds more completely before being able to heal those of others? That moment still seems like yesterday now as I write about it. It was a moment suspended in time, in which I finally started to find true purpose through our son's pain, which had brought me to healing my own pain.

It was around this time that I decided to have my own personal therapy session with Edith, and we explored my story in the sand tray. To this day, the immense therapeutic power of this projective technique has remained crystal clear for me due to the depth of emotion it released in me, as well as the insight I gained into the way forward on my healing journey. I left with a deep sense of knowing that I would find the strength to confront my father and to complete my play therapy internship. Furthermore, and most significantly, I would intuitively know when I was ready to take these two important steps, and I could not impose a time frame on it at all. The sand tray image that I created is presented in Figure 14.

Figure 14
My sand tray play therapy

That same evening, I received a message that our request for funding for an Activity Programme at the Old Age Home where I was working had been unexpectedly rejected in its final stage. I had been hopeful and excited about re-initiating the programme, and I felt deeply disappointed at the rejection. Up to that point, I seemed to have been shown so many signs that it was the way forward for me, although I was struggling to see how I could manage the extra work and time commitments while also wanting to train in play therapy for the longer-term future. Retrospectively, I can now see how one door closed and another opened to me on exactly the same day. However, the door that had opened for me, showing me both the direction and the specific route to follow, had found me through my pain – it was definitely not going to be the easiest one to walk through, but it was certainly the most fulfilling one, and the one most true to my new sense of purpose.

I remember sitting in that seminar room a few weeks later, feeling like an excited child who was waking up on the day that she was finally returning home after a long time away. The psychologist opened the seminar with an incredibly powerful optical illusion, being symbolic of the irreversible shift in perspective needed to truly understand problem sexual behaviour. That optical illusion has stayed close to my heart and soul, and I recently used it myself in my presentation about my own healing journey in a "Moving Beyond" occupational therapy training workshop!

At the start of the seminar on Children with Problem Sexual Behaviours I realised that, amidst my excitement, I had forgotten to bring my exam pad paper. However, in looking through my bag for my exam pad, I discovered my big black hard-covered A4-sized exercise book, which I was using at the time to write this book. I turned to the back of the exercise book to make my notes. Looking back, I realise why this seemingly insignificant memory has remained with me so clearly. While transferring the seminar notes from the back of my book to a file for my internship training, I started to see the picture revealed to me, as more of the jigsaw puzzle fell into place. This cheap, rather tatty-looking black book that I had carried around with me in my bag for a number of months now carried not only my past but my future too. My past and future were written at both ends of the same book – my future was not deterministically defined by my past, but rather my past constantly re-shaped, re-created, and re-coloured my future into an ever-changing, new and beautiful design. This dynamic process of transformation was happening in the moment – it is the gift of the present. Now, as I continue writing my book at my computer eighteen months later, I am once again humbled by its beginnings, and I occasionally still return to pen and paper – an easier medium through which my soul can speak.

Although the internship opportunity had opened the door for me to walk through, I was unable to pursue the opportunity at the time, due to having to support Joshua through his own healing journey and the time, personal stress and financial constraints that resulted from it. I spoke to Edith, his play therapist, who encouraged me to take more time to heal both myself and my son before embarking on the internship. Now, approximately two years later, I have finally surrendered and chosen to complete the writing of my book before starting the internship. Divine providence has once again intervened to reveal its unseen plan to ensure that the wounded healer in me is more fully healed before moving on to healing the wounds of others.

21

A NEW PERSPECTIVE

Hazel

asually, I sat down to catch up on reading my WhatsApp messages. Little did I know that what I was about to view on the tiny screen held a secret seed to my healing ... a seed of grace from which understanding could slowly start to germinate into forgiveness of my mother. This secret seed had been held captive underground in the dark, dry, infertile soil of my mother's intolerable pain. Now, finally, divine providence was intervening, allowing it to reveal itself, and enabling the next generation in our family to find healing at last.

It was a few months after the seminar and my brother Mark had sent me WhatsApp messages with copies of photos from my mother's childhood family photo album. As I flipped through the old black and white photos, I felt the somewhat familiar feeling of time suddenly standing still as my world moved in slow motion and I became disconnected from the world around me. My suspicions were confirmed when I saw the last few photos of my mother as an early adolescent. She was naked, with her pre-pubescent breasts exposed, and she was sitting in a posed position with her legs subtly hiding her genitals. I felt the shame etched into her eyes in one specific photo – her shame, which she had never been able to face, had now become my shame.

These photos followed one of her, at about three years of age, in an open field – with just a small woolly jumper on, lifting it up with her hands, exposing her completely naked body below. This picture sank into a place somewhere very deep in me and I am still not quite sure which nerve it hit, but it is releasing tears in me right now as I type these words. Was I about this age when I was sexually abused myself? I am no longer searching for that answer … just allowing my tears to flow as they finally start to release my pain from my mother's pain.

Another photo was of my mother as a young girl in a pretty dress, standing alongside her father. She seemed somewhat uncomfortable in his presence, with an awkward, uneasy look on her face. What strikes me now, looking at this picture again, apart from my mother's facial expression, is that at first glance I could not see her arms. It was as if the short sleeves on her dress didn't have any arms coming out of them. As I enlarged the photo to see whether her arms were tucked behind her back (as I had assumed they were), I realised that it was just an optical illusion, caused by a shadow in the picture hiding her arms, and more light exposing her hands. I am immediately transported back to my own childhood drawing of stick figures with no arms. Could that shadow now also be reflecting the sense of helplessness and disempowerment depicted in my own childhood drawings of sexual abuse? Why was it the first thing I seemed to notice when looking at her photo? We seemed to be shadows of each other as young children. I am needing to breathe deeply now and, once again, allow my tears to flow. I had misconceived this as being an easy chapter to write in my story.

As I collected my thoughts together again after my tears had been released, my only-too-familiar sense of self-doubt started to raise its voice. Were my brother and I perhaps just reading too much into these photos, in our desperate attempt to find the missing piece in the jigsaw puzzle that could explain why my mother is who she is today? I decided that I needed to share these photos with my husband, with a trusted friend, and with Louise to help me answer this question. Everyone I showed them to had the same response to different degrees – from judging the photos to be totally inappropriate for a family photo album, to considering them to be pornographic photos that must have been taken and placed in the album by her mother, her father, or a close family member. My mother's tragic story was finally unfolding.

Mark and I spoke with my older brother, who had also seen the photos, and together we decided that we needed to speak to my mother about what we had found. But how were we to approach her when she had clearly locked away her shameful secret her whole life and had projected it onto her own children as a way of avoiding it herself? Would our confrontation simply push her into further denial, or would it cause her to have a major breakdown? If she were to break down, would we support her? Could we support her after what she had put us through? The answer to this last question was clear: if we were to confront her and she were to break down, it would then be our responsibility to support her.

My head knew that confronting my mother would be the right thing to do, but my heart also knew that, at that stage, I had too much of my own pain and would not be able to support her. My head also argued at times with my heart, saying that my mother had chosen not to confront her own pain. She had made a personal choice and we, as her children, had suffered abuse as a result of her choices. I wondered why I should support her in her pain when she had caused me so much pain and trauma and had left me alone to suffer with it in my own darkness.

Mark and I finally decided that we did need to speak to my mother about the photos we had found but that, instead of con- fronting her with them directly, we needed to gently offer her an opportunity to be able to speak about her abuse if she chose to. We were fairly certain that her level of denial would not change and that, by confronting her directly with the photos, we would almost certainly only deepen her denial. We decided we would tell her that we had found an old family photo album of hers and wondered why we had never been shown any of her own childhood photos; we would take it gently from there without pressuring her too much. However, we all had a lot going on in our lives at that particular time, so we decided to let it lie for a while, as we needed to find the right time to meet with her personally – this was not something to discuss on Skype or over the internet.

Time passed by in our busy lives, leaving little opportunity for the two of us to speak to my mother. Without realising it, a deep sense of intuition was slowly growing in me – a sense that we had found the photos for the purposes of our own healing, rather than to open up my mother's wounds in the pursuit of the "truth" we felt that we had a right to know. Slowly we realised that we did not need to confront my mother with these photos, and so we chose not to. These photos spoke a truth, and nothing more needed to be known about their message for us to be able to heal.

You might wonder how Mark managed to access the photos that my mother would have preferred to have kept a deeply hidden secret. Mark had spent the night in the spare room at my other brother's house and had noticed that a drawer of my parents' old cupboard was taped closed on the outside, despite it not being broken. This sent a little alarm bell ringing for him, so he opened the drawer and found my mother's old childhood photo album, which contained the photos that told the tragic story of her sexual abuse as a child. It came at a time for me when old dreams and drawings had started to bring me to the realisation that my mother had probably not just been a silent witness in my sexual abuse, but that she must also have had at least some level of involvement in it. It was also a crucial time in which I needed to move towards making peace with my mother in my heart, because reconciliation with her, at that moment, seemed impossible. I realise once again that it must have been divine providence that guided Mark towards finding these photos at that specific time.

At just the time I needed it most, I had been given this seed of grace that offered me a new perspective on my mother. As I look at these photos again, while writing this chapter, I realise how this new perspective has enabled me to start to feel some level of compassion for her. In a recent "Moving Beyond" workshop, I cried intensely as I spoke about my mother's pain during a role play therapy session. I seemed to be experiencing the grief that she had never allowed herself to feel. In that moment of grace, I further released myself towards being able to truly forgive her. The tears I have cried in writing this chapter are for her – the tears she never cried.

My mother made the bad choices that she made because she did not have the personal strength or support system to face her own pain. My brother and I have been able to find the strength not to make those bad choices or to continue the cycle of abuse. We have been fortunate to have each other's love and support, as well as the support of our partners and other friends, in facing our pain, which resulted from her pain. My mother had no support at all and has quite possibly kept this painful secret to herself her whole life and never told anyone. What a tragedy! I would like to be able to say that I would not have made the same bad choices that she made if I had found myself under the same circumstances. However, if I were deeply honest with myself, could I ever be one hundred percent certain in guaranteeing this? I don't think so.

I would like to conclude this chapter by sharing with you the words I expressed during a group feedback session towards the end of a recent "Moving Beyond" occupational therapy workshop at which I presented my own personal healing journey. As I write this now, my tears start to flow again, blurring my computer screen … "I forgive you for not moving through your own darkness."

22

THE CONFRONTATION

Hazel

Awhile after Mark had sent me my mother's childhood photos, I made a firm decision that I was not yet ready to confront my father. My fear and anxiety still felt stronger than my courage when a totally unexpected opportunity arose to visit my second-oldest brother, Derrick, for two days, where my parents lived. I was exhausted and had not seen Derrick for more than two years. I did not want to destroy this invaluable time by seeing my parents, as I had already decided to confront my father the next time that I saw my parents.

Our first stop on the twelve-hour drive with my youngest brother, Mark, was the Lord Milner Hotel in Matjiesfontein. Built in 1899, it is reputed to be haunted by ghosts, one of which is believed to be the ghost of a wounded British soldier. We were sitting enjoying breakfast when Mark told me that it was the exact place where he and Derrick (my middle brother) had been when another family member had spoken for the first time of how an older boy had touched her on her private parts when she was younger. The first ghost of the next generation of our family had come to life there in that one-hundred-and-eighteen-year-old building in the middle of nowhere. I started to talk about my growing fear that I would be haunted by my own ghost for an indefinite period of time until another opportunity arose for me to see my parents again. Time and distance limited my opportunities for that, and my parents were getting older. It had haunted me for more than a year and the fear had crept into my very bones. Perhaps my wounded inner child had gone to gain strength from the ghost of the wounded British soldier at the Lord Milner Hotel, to release her to fly free once more. Mark told me that the tiny chapel in the garden was a place where, in the past, he had found he could talk to God, and he suggested that I go into the chapel. (See Figure 15.)

Figure 15
The chapel at the Lord Milner Hotel, Matjiesfontein
"Let go and let me speak"

I sat in solitude in the chapel, trying to meditate. I struggled for peace of mind amidst circular thoughts and waves of anxiety from which I could find no safe distance within my centre. In the midst of the crashing waves, I heard the words, "Let go and let me speak", with crystalline clarity. I knew then, without any uncertainty, that I was going to confront my father the next day, with the help of my guardian angel. Momentarily, I felt my strength returning to me, with a sense that I was being enfolded in the wings of my guardian angel.

As we continued driving, after our stop at Matjiesfontein, my soul once again seemed to shift back into the passenger seat, making space for my anxiety to take control in the driver's seat. After Joshua had fallen asleep in the back of the car, reality hit hard as Mark and I took the opportunity to talk about how to focus the upcoming conversation of confrontation, step by step, from beginning to end. This included talking about recording the conversation and exactly how and when to do that. Mark and I had previously spoken about the importance of recording the conversation; something that he had done himself when he had confronted his abuser many years prior to that. We felt that it was important, as it may be necessary for resolving any potential future conflict of opinions regarding exactly what was said during the conversation, and it could serve as a source of evidence in that respect. It could also be something that I may want to reflect on myself. However, I was not aware at the time that, in fact, it was against the law to record a conversation without the other person's permission.

As I shifted towards its outer edges, the vortex of my anxiety threatened to obscure my vision of the road ahead through the windscreen, as if I was driving in a storm without windscreen wipers. Towards the end of the journey, Mark needed a break after having done all of the driving, so we swapped seats and I took the driver's seat. Much to his dismay, I moved into the slow lane. Fortunately, he was too tired to argue. However, I very gradually became aware that the emptiness at the centre of my vortex was what would enable me to control the vehicle and remain focused. This emptiness began to transform into an invisible source of strength, guiding the steering wheel from its centre, rather than through my hands at its circumference. As my vortex still obscured my vision of the road ahead, I needed to trust the centre of the steering wheel, let my hands relax on its circumference, and listen carefully to the navigator. We finally arrived safely, with tremendous excitement at our reunion after two years, to enjoy dinner at a local restaurant. Joshua was the centre of attention, amidst much laughter, as he decided to feed his long-lost uncle his dinner!

After a totally sleepless night, I awoke with a sense of dread ... that day was *the* day. How would I ever remember the stages through which I needed to move in focusing the conversation of confrontation? Surely everything I had discussed with Mark was going to fly out of the window at the most critical moment of the conversation. How would I even be focused enough to remember to turn on the recorder of the cell phone before starting the conversation? My head was taking control as I approached the outer edges of my vortex and I felt as if I had been run over by a train at full speed. My neck and upper back were about to explode with muscle spasms. Mark told me to stop worrying about Joshua's wet pants and to gather my strength in solitude in the garden, so I insisted on his quick osteopathy magic for my back. Fortunately, Derrick's wife kindly took over the care of Joshua.

As we drove around the block one last time before meeting my parents, I struggled immensely for clarity and focus, the volume of my thoughts seemingly drowned out by the sound of my heartbeat, in a sea of anxiety. Momentarily, a pearl was washed ashore as Mark squeezed my hand when I got out of the car, saying that he knew that I could do what needed to be done. Somehow, I grabbed the pearl before it was washed back to sea, and I put one foot in front of the other, approaching my parents.

My whole world seemed to move in a blurred sense of slow motion when I looked towards my father. I slowly became aware of this rather pathetic, sad, fragile old man as I approached him. With each step that closed the distance between us, I recaptured a fleeting glimpse of the pearl that I was still holding in my hand, as I tightened my grip on it.

GETTING STARTED

Half an hour passed in what seemed like a re-awakening of a distant past incarnation, while we made superficial conversation. I glanced around at pictures from my childhood home that were now hanging on the walls around me; pictures through which my own ghost began to materialise. I glanced at my watch and realised that I had exceeded the time limit to refocus the conversation and take control of that ghost. When it started to feel as if my anxiety was taking control of me, I somehow intuitively knew that the first step towards taking control needed to be a physical one. I managed to stand up what felt like seconds before the walls collapsed in on me. Shakily, my body responded as I put one foot in front of the other on my way to the toilet and then set up my cell phone for recording before returning to the lounge. It seemed that the simple physical process of moving to the toilet had initiated the building of a bridge between my mind and my soul. However, as I sat down again, strategically positioning my handbag with the recording cell phone in it, that bridge seemed to collapse, opening up a wide canyon with only a threadbare tightrope to cross over. I almost heard myself asking my father to move a bit closer so that I could hear him properly, as there was something important that I needed to talk about. My words felt disconnected when they spluttered disjointedly out of my mouth. A fleeting and yet familiar sense of panic flew through me. Was I on the edge of dissociating? Was the simple physical process of talking now creating a chasm between my mind and my body? I felt as if I was reliving a tandem parachute jump. My mind was screaming with fear and anxiety, yet my soul knew exactly what I had to do. I only needed to hang on tight and trust my instructor to remain in control. I had set myself the challenge of overcoming my strongest fear – my fear of confronting my father – and at that moment, my mind needed to surrender control to my soul and just hang on tight! Seconds before the point of starting the conversation, I felt as if I had just exited the plane and was somersaulting through the air, totally out of control, and consumed with fear.

GETTING TO THE POINT OF NO RETURN

I opened the conversation by expressing to my father that my primary intention was one of self-healing and re-empowerment, rather than revenge, rage and retaliation. While moving on to explain that over many years I had come to know that I had been sexually abused, my senses were all telling me that I was still in free fall, and I had no sense of being attached to the safety of my instructor, or of being able to listen to my guardian angel. When my father asked me who it was that had abused me, I felt that I was finally starting to regain some strength. Without being aware of it at the time, I think I must have reconnected with my guardian angel. In a single, unforgettable moment, it was as if she had allowed me to extend my arms under her wings at last, taking the flight position rather than the fear position, while she briefly held my hands, guiding me before letting go again. Without hesitation, I managed to calmly answer that it was my father who had abused me. He expressed no obvious sense of shock, rage or emotional distress while asking me on what I had based my conclusion that he was responsible for my abuse. While explaining how I had come to this conclusion, waves of anxiety washed over me, but I seemed more able to let them come and go, rather than being washed away with them. A part of me knew then that I had come through the most difficult part of that conversation.

My father then shared that he was very pleased that I had decided to speak to him in the way that I had, as he hoped that it would relieve the pressure on me. We agreed that I would email further specific details on how I had come to know that he was responsible for my abuse. I further confirmed that I had absolutely no doubt of the truth of my accusation, and that I hoped that he could find some peace with that in his own way. I affirmed that, while I could, I had no intention of trying to take the matter further; I only wished to find peace and closure. I started to feel a renewed sense of empowerment as the words flowed more easily from me; somehow, they were feeding my lost sense of strength. Little did I know at the time that my recording of that conversation with my father would serve as a turning point for Thomas, my eldest brother, in temporarily shifting his opinion on my accusation against my father.

Throughout that part of the conversation, my mother continually interjected, pressuring me to immediately give concrete evidence and details of what had happened in my abuse. As she interrupted us, she seemed totally devoid of any emotion – she had an old, and yet somehow familiar, cold, stony glare on her face, and an insistent, subtly threatening tone in her voice. My father also repeatedly stated that I must be quoting what the psychologist had put into my head, or that what I was saying must be coming from either Thomas or Mark. I found the strength to remain calm, and I reiterated many times that I would put it all in an email and that I wanted, at all costs, to avoid an explosive confrontation by not going into those details during our present conversation. Furthermore, I reminded my parents continually that it was a conclusion that I had ultimately come to myself, with support from professionals. My father also asked whether my accusation was entirely directed at him, or whether any of it was directed towards my mother. Only later would I come to more fully understand the significance of that question and how it was, in fact, an answer in itself. A few dreams and old drawings had told me that my mother had had a role to play in my abuse, but I had decided to keep her out of it for the moment, as time alone would reveal more on exactly what her role had been.

BEYOND NO RETURN

After further circular conversation around the issue of concrete evidence, my father finally expressed a wish that, at the end of it all, we would be able to remain friends, if that was what we both wanted. That was a turning point for me, as if my instructor, in an unforgettable moment, had finally opened the main parachute and I felt completely safe. The words flowed from me, "It is immensely hard to forgive without acknowledgment. If that doesn't happen, it makes my healing process immeasurably harder ... I am now in a place where I would like to be able to forgive you ..." My anxiety had completely subsided and shifted into the passenger seat. I was once again in the driver's seat, feeling at ease and in complete control. I felt my sense of self and truth growing stronger from my centre as I spoke.

Somehow this seemed to ease the tension between my father and myself as he went on to say that he was pleased that I had opened up in the way that I had, followed by, "When I say that I can't remember, it means I can't remember. I am not saying that I didn't do it." A moment of self-doubt crept in ... Was I hearing him properly? I then confirmed twice to him what I understood him to be saying – that his not remembering some specific details didn't necessarily mean that he didn't do it. Very shortly after this, he continued by saying that the fact that he couldn't remember did also not necessarily mean that he did do it – that it only meant that he can't remember. In a flash, an old and yet-too-familiar sense of craziness started to take hold of me again, threatening my sense of safety and control with a thick cloud of self-doubt and confusion, completely blurring my vision of the way ahead. Although I was oblivious to it at the time, I believe that my guardian angel must have drawn very close to me at that point, helping me to find the courage to repeat to my father that my intention was not to attack and hurt him, but rather to heal myself. He seemed more at ease then, expressing that he entirely accepted that my intention was to heal myself and that I should take my time in sending all the specific details to him in an e-mail. I once more returned to my source of strength beneath the wings of my guardian angel.

I regained my clear vision of the way ahead from there as my father went on to tell me how pleased he was that we had had that conversation. He expressed his understanding of the circumstantial difficulties that had made it impossible for us to have more time together with each other to discuss the matter further on a more personal level. He followed on with these words to me, "I admire you for doing so. It must have taken quite a lot of guts on your part to actually bring this whole subject up." I am once again grateful to my father for finding the strength to say these words to me, as I later mentioned in a letter to him. That was the beginning of me finding my peace.

As I now move between writing and occasionally listening to our recorded conversation, I feel as if I am hovering on the edge of another emotional storm of grief. I am fighting an overwhelming sense of loss over where things have come to now with my father since our confrontation. I want to trust that my writing can allow me to release my tears, but I am in the wrong place – a restaurant with no privacy. Finally, I find a hiding place down in the garden and let my tears flow while I speak to Louise over the phone.

PEACE AT LAST

My synchronised flight with my guardian angel was drawing towards an end as I assertively deflected my mother's continual, increasingly forceful, repeated attempts to pressurise me to immediately share concrete evidence backing up my accusation. We had already agreed that the information would be e-mailed in my own time, and I was not prepared to continue along that line of conversation any further.

My father went on to repeat how pleased he was that I had brought up the matter, whether or not he was guilty of what I was accusing him of. Seemingly flowing from this were his words, "We are closer together now than we were before you brought this up. In the last fifteen minutes or so since you've been talking to me, we have gotten a lot, lot closer." I experienced a sense of peace enveloping me. I did not know at the time whether that peace could ever close the distance between my father and myself through any level of reconciliation; only time would reveal that answer. However, what I sensed very strongly was that it was an immensely huge relief for him, and I knew that I was finding the peace within myself that I needed to heal.

As I finally stood up and started walking towards the door, my mother started questioning me on who knew about it, how long they had known for, and how much they knew. Why was she choosing to ask me this if nothing had happened to me? As my mother and I departed from the flat, she said to my father, "Hubby, I love you." When I heard these words, in a flash, I felt physically sick and wanted to throw up everything that was inside me. The feeling subsided as quickly as it had emerged, and it was followed by an intuition that I needed to be silent and say nothing at all. In that silence, the first thing she said to me was that she was truly shocked and that she wanted me to know with no uncertainty that she knew absolutely nothing about it. Her voice and face were totally devoid of emotion.

Just before getting to the gate, I knew that I somehow had to try to make peace with my mother too by asking her whether she had ever been sexually abused herself as a child. She confirmed that she had and told me about a man in the park who had sexually abused her. (In the past she had also shared with my brother's psychiatrist that a man on the bus had shown her his penis.) When I went on to ask her whether anyone in the family had ever sexually abused her, her immediate and very defensive response was that her father and her stepfather had never touched her. I can clearly recall the moment when she raised her voice in making this statement while wagging her finger in the air. I sensed a subtle level of anger in her, behind which there lay intolerable pain. At that moment, I knew that my mother had definitely been sexually abused by her father and also, quite possibly, by her stepfather too. Why else would she specifically mention her stepfather when there were so many others that she could have mentioned? She had remained in deep denial over it. In response to her denials, I shared with her that, sadly, the photos that we had found of her in her family album told a very sad and different story from what she had just told me. Before allowing any further conflict to emerge between us, I said goodbye to her and went to join my brothers who were waiting for me outside in the car.

As I climbed into the car, I was enveloped in a huge sense of relief, together with a level of sadness. Was I feeling my mother's sadness at that moment?

Although a lot was still unknown to my conscious mind, the answers I needed at the time to find my peace had been provided. I could not have hoped for a better outcome with my father at that point in time. I had also managed to confirm my suspicions about my mother's past. In time this would be the medicine I needed to forgive her.

I don't believe that confrontation of your abuser is an essential and necessary part of the healing process, although it can potentially be empowering. It is not at all the only way to find ultimate peace and closure, as our healing journeys are all unique. We all walk different paths towards finding peace, and my footsteps will follow a different route to yours. We can never walk in each other's footsteps to try and find our own way.

Writing about this now, I realise that in my confrontation with my parents I had been living the words spoken to me at the chapel, "Let go and let me speak". I will always be deeply grateful that my guardian angel inspired me with the right words to find the answers that I needed to heal. Beyond that, she had given me the strength to surrender to her, to move through my anxiety, and to find calmness and a clear, focused state of mind to confront my father peacefully. Without her, this would never have been possible.

I sincerely hope that, in sharing with you my journey of confronting my father, I am able to reach out and touch you, leaving you with a sense of knowing that healing is always possible, especially if you surrender to God – in whatever form you perceive God to be.

23

VICTIMS AND PERPETRATORS: SHADOW WORK

Louise

S hadow work is a significant step in our spiritual growth. The concept of shadow work is a difficult one. Often, we are so trapped in our false self and in the worldly view of reality that shadow work initially trips us all up. We want to make everything, including ourselves, "good", "perfect" and "beautiful". However, this is not real. Shadow work is about embracing shadows as they are, without trying to change them to appear better.

Everything in life has a contrary element: good and bad; perfection and imperfection; beauty and ugliness; and pain and joy. By limiting our view to the positive elements, we reject or deny the depth that the negative elements afford us. In their book, *The Gift of Pain*, Philip Yancey and Dr Paul Brand make a case that the reason Western society has so many depressed or unhappy people, is that we shun any inkling of pain. Yet pain and joy are two sides of the same coin. The depth to which we are able to experience and sit with pain is equal to the depth to which we can experience joy. Another analogy we can use is that of choosing to see the world only through hues of white – this does not work, because we need the black hues to provide the depth and dimensions in any painting. Through shadow work, we realise that in all the characteristics that we deny, we simultaneously deny their positive elements. In shadow work, we call it "the gift". For example, the gift of being mistrusting is that it can prevent us from being conned. Wanting to be trusting of all people all the time could be detrimental to us or our families. However, this does not mean that we are to be mistrusting all the time. It is important to embrace trusting with all its gifts, and also to embrace mistrusting with all its gifts; to be able to balance the two, and to be trusting or mistrusting, as is most fitting in any given circumstance.

As children, we learn through feedback from significant people in our lives which behaviour is acceptable and which behaviour is not. Systematically, we suppress the unacceptable behaviour more and more in order to be loved and accepted by the important people in our lives. On the other hand, we daily strive to portray or possess the acceptable behaviour. After a while, we are convinced that exhibiting the unacceptable behaviour means that we ourselves are unacceptable. This behaviour or characteristic becomes a "no-go" zone for us and if others portray this behaviour, they are considered to be "no-go" people. We judge them and have strong negative reactions towards them. Ironically, the healing of our old wounds is often wrapped up in getting to know and understand these people.

There is a saying in shadow work that we all carry inside us a little Hitler and a little Mother Teresa. It suits us to classify people as totally good or totally bad. It makes life easier for us if we categorise people and then just mingle with the good ones. After all, we always consider ourselves to be in the good or correct category. Unfortunately, life is not that easy. Part of our journey is to realise that all people have good and bad in them; it is just the same with us. It is so easy for us to say now that there was nothing good about Hitler. However, there were more Nobel prize winners from Hitler's Germany than from any other country at any other time in the twentieth century. We all have the potential at any stage to be both a Hitler and a Mother Teresa; both have good elements, and both have "bad" elements. In shadow work, we also have what is termed a "light" shadow. We have brilliant aspects of ourselves that we have suppressed, and we believe they are not acceptable or good enough.

The ultimate aim of shadow work is for us to claim back all aspects of ourselves, without judging them as "good" or "bad", and to embrace all that we are. We no longer attempt to be perfect, which is what our false self is constantly trying to achieve. Instead, we strive to be whole. As we are confronted with our "imperfections" and "bad" aspects, we become humble and let go of judgment, realizing more clearly that we are all the same, despite status, possession, etc. We are all wounded people. This truth became strikingly clear through Hazel's journey.

When we hear that someone has been sexually abused, we are very quick to condemn the perpetrator. If we can classify them as all "bad", we automatically exempt ourselves from being in any way similar to the perpetrators. We can then condemn and judge. The boundaries between the two extremes of "perpetrator" and "victim" are obvious and wide. But what if we asked the question differently? What if we asked: "Did you ever use sexuality for a bad purpose?" All I've done is to define abuse as the dictionary does. Does your answer change now? So, have you to any degree been "guilty" of sexual abuse? How wide is the gap between victim and perpetrator now? Where would you place yourself?

Before I continue with Hazel's story, I would like to interrupt this chapter and recount a story of another client of mine. She had been sexually abused for many years by her best friend's brother, who also happened to be their neighbour. When the abuse started, she was eight years old and he was a young adolescent boy. When she became a client of mine, she was in her thirties. She contacted me and asked to do shadow work. We started by identifying all her shadows (those parts of herself that she had rejected). Not surprisingly, the shadow of a sexual abuser was one of her shadows. By making use of psychodrama techniques, I placed her into the chair of the sexual abuser. She started to cry uncontrollably. She couldn't talk. She gasped as she tried to communicate with me. She was distorted. Thinking it was too difficult for her. I took her out of the role and placed her back into being her thirty-five-year-old self. In her thirty-five-year-old role, she was shaken but emotionally stable and cognisant. We talked about the experience and she asked to go back to the perpetrator's role, where she had the exact same response as previously. I allowed her the space to cry as much as she needed. This experience brought her to a place of embracing the perpetrator. Afterwards, she explained that she had never felt so broken before and she realised how broken a sexual abuser must be to be able to abuse someone in that way. We ended the session with a conversation between her True Self and the sexual abuser. It was a sacred moment, filled with beauty and deep divine wisdom … and forgiveness. She realised that although she would never condone or fully understand the sexual abuse as an act, she could understand the level of desperation and brokenness that brings all people to do things of which they are deeply ashamed.

In Hazel's story, the lines between victim and perpetrator are blurred. How do you categorise all family members and then love or hate them according to the category they are in? There is her three-year-old boy, Joshua, who was expelled from his preschool due to an act of sexual abuse. So, is he a victim or perpetrator? If he is the victim, what about the girl he sexually abused? What is she? What about the boy who first exposed Joshua to this unnatural sexual behaviour? Is he the perpetrator? Yet, no child younger than three knows about penetration without having been exposed to it. So, is he the victim?

Does any of this reasoning change in any way if the people are adults? As Hazel's story unfolds, we are confronted with a mother and father who, by their own admission, were accomplices in the sexual abuse of their third son, Mark, when he was a young adult. They actively encouraged the sexual abuse of their son by his choirmaster. It seems totally sick and unfathomable. It is so easy to condemn and judge them, distance ourselves from them, and convince ourselves that we are superior, better than they are. Upon questioning further, and through divine providence,

Hazel found photos of her mother as a young pre-pubescent girl, posing naked for a photo, the look in her eyes giving away her discomfort with the situation; that and her body language of shame. It is suspected that the photos had been taken by her father, Hazel's maternal grandfather. Is Hazel's mother the victim or the perpetrator? The background of Hazel's father is hazy, with minimal available information. There is no hard-core "evidence" for us to place him in a specific category. So, what do we do instinctively? Give him the benefit of the doubt and view him as a victim too, or see him as a perpetrator, and judge and hate him? Where do we even begin to make sense of all of this? Does it not bring us to a place of questioning our own need to label and classify; our need to love or hate? After all, all people are merely projections of our own selves in a small or a big way. We see the world as we are, not as it is.

In conclusion, the hardest part of shadow work is the embracing of all that appears to be "bad", knowing that somewhere, somehow, there is something good in all of it – even if we haven't found its gift yet; that and holding paradoxes. We naturally want to simplify things and choose either/or, but the most difficult part of life is being able to hold a paradox. We need to hold a paradox without feeling compelled to choose any side; to let go of judgement and to love instead; to be confronted with ourselves, totally whole, with all the good and the bad, and to be OK with it. When we can manage this, we move away from our false self and start living more authentically from our True Self.

READER'S REFLECTION:

Reflect on those "types" of people that you love to hate: the abusers, snobs, homosexuals, super-rich, drug addicts, or homeless. Is there something about their character that you fear in yourself and don't want to embrace? Go out and find someone like that. Without judgement, have a deep conversation with them and just listen to their stories. Has your perception of them changed in any way? Has your perception of yourself changed in any way?

24

GUARDIAN ANGEL PSYCHODRAMA

Hazel

I had been feeling surprisingly calm and emotionally detached while tracing the drawing I found in my old childhood scrapbook and transferring it onto my computer. I somehow felt that perhaps this chapter would be easier than I had predicted. A few days later, I opened the folder on my computer and placed the cursor below the picture, ready to start writing.

As my fingers reached for the keyboard, waves of anxiety with the power of a tsunami suddenly threatened to capsize me. As the waves hit me, I felt as if I had been thrown over the side of my tiny raft, far from the shore. Somewhere amidst the waves, I recalled some other pictures that I had drawn during a Holotropic Breathwork workshop when I was a Psychology Honours student. Without a lifejacket, I was clinging on for dear life to the edge of the raft that was sinking. Before I sank and drowned, I shut down my computer, closed the lid firmly, walked away and distracted myself with something completely different. Before long, my feet hit the ground again on the floor of my raft and I found that the tsunami had passed. I tried to write again sometime soon after that, but my raft started capsizing again. I felt immensely frustrated that I was unable to continue with writing this chapter, and I considered simply moving onto a different chapter instead; a diversion tactic of mine that had been successful in the past. However, this time I decided that I needed to try to take the direct route, so I contacted Louise and arranged a time to meet with her.

I remember clearly that we met on a Friday afternoon at the end of the day. I was tired and suspected that Louise probably was too, so I suggested that we rather just have a social chat instead of the serious conversation we had planned. I just wasn't in the mood for anything else. Despite that, I agreed to start off with a short conversation about what I was struggling with. I nonchalantly handed Louise the other old pictures that I had found. As I briefly shared my experience of the tsunami and my immense frustration with the block it had caused for my writing, I simply reiterated that perhaps, for the moment, I should take the diversion route into another chapter.

I still felt somewhat emotionally detached while we talked about the fact that one of the pictures seemed to confirm that there had been someone female who had abused me. I had sus-pected that my mother had been involved in my abuse. Could this be her? Still, I was debating the matter in my head, as if I was asking someone else to move my piece on a chessboard, on my behalf. I was observing and participating in the game from a very safe distance, not touching any of the playing pieces myself. Was I perhaps one step closer to checkmate? It didn't matter, because someone else was playing for me. I remember Louise trying to ask me what the very large, widely open mouth in one of the drawings possibly meant to me. When I said that it seemed to be screaming, she asked me what it wanted to say, instead of screaming. My mind was blank for a while before I said, "Stop." Saying the word evoked no emotion, although I was acutely aware of my rapidly escalating anxiety levels as she asked me to try to finish the sentence – "Stop what?" We were going around in circles and I felt nothing at all except for my hand that was hanging over the side of the chair, shaking. I just couldn't seem to stop shaking. I agreed to try a different approach with some psychodrama, for no reason other than that it might help me to get over my writer's block.

Initially we set the scene of me writing my book, following on with different scenes of role reversal incorporating me acting out the roles of my inner child, my anxiety, and my adult self, seated facing each other. I clearly recall liaising with my anxiety as my adult self, as I quite quickly started to shift out of a completely detached emotional space towards a space where I touched on quite intense feelings of frustration and anger at both my adult self and my anxiety. I could not break free from my own trap as my anxiety retaliated against any attempts from my adult self to shift out of the way, by simply increasing its strength. I was fighting a losing battle and remained trapped in a vicious whirlwind as my argument between my adult self and my anxiety escalated, with no sense of resolution. I was once again at the outer edges of the whirlwind, with no sense of being able to find calmness at its centre. Although not aware of it at the time, I had lost my soul compass.

I recall Louise asking me, in the midst of the intensifying battle, "Where is your sanity in all of this?" For a fleeting moment, I stood dead still on the battlefield and wondered what she meant by that. She followed on by asking who could help me in the battle. Without any hesitation, I immediately replied that my guardian angel could help me. I was gently washed over by a wave carrying an old memory that I knew I had somehow never lost, but simply forgotten about. However, this time the wave was emerging from deep within me rather than closing in on me from the outside. Rather than being washed away by this wave, I started to allow myself to flow with it.

I positioned my guardian angel standing up on a chair above and behind my inner child, who herself was seated behind my anxiety, with my adult self now seated opposite my anxiety.

Next, Louise asked my adult self to come and take the seat of my inner child behind my anxiety, in front of my guardian angel. As soon as I sat down in my inner child's seat, tears flowed intensely from the depths of my being. I became an eternal river of uncontained grief, flowing with enormous magnitude over a waterfall. I felt only vaguely aware of Louise's voice as she encouraged me to breathe deeply, while my torrent of tears continued to flow. There were no thoughts going through my mind at all at the time; I had left my mind far behind and had embraced my inner child and her raw pain. Actually, I had moved beyond embracing her; I had become her.

Following on from there, Louise asked my inner child to talk to my guardian angel and ask her anything she wanted to know from her. The words flowed spontaneously from me as I asked her why she had let me be sexually abused. As I moved into the role of my guardian angel standing on the chair above my inner child, I seemed to become completely enveloped by a warm blanket of absolute peace and serenity as my hands and lower arms started to feel energised with a strong sensation of pins and needles. The peace and serenity were somehow imbued with a long-lost sense of familiarity that I could not quite define.

As my guardian angel, I reassured my inner child that I could not do anything to prevent her from being sexually abused. However, I assured her that I had always been with her and would continue to be with her. I could guide her into the future, transforming her trauma through her writing, and helping others through their similar pain too.

I became filled with empathy and love for my inner child in an unforgettably powerful moment; I experienced a feeling that was somehow beyond the limited words of this world. I vividly recall having to take things very slowly in coming back to the present and reconnecting with my body. I had to take Louise's hand to balance myself as I stepped off the chair, back onto the ground. Once again, it felt as if I had somehow become my guardian angel, rather than just being a channel for her. As I write now, I feel the same sensation of pins and needles starting to flow in my hands and fingers – an immensely healing energy, which I believe is drawn from a divine source.

As the scene continued unfolding, Louise asked me to shift back into my adult self and speak to my inner child. I recall vividly, as if it was yesterday, being once again overwhelmed with tears of grief as I struggled to utter the words, "I love you." While I type now, those tears are welling up again as I reconnect with that experience. Retrospectively, I now realise that my adult self could not embrace my inner child and love her. She was too frightened of feeling her pain and the depth of her woundedness. My tears were perhaps starting to release that fear, as I found strength by reuniting with my guardian angel to embrace my inner child, as well as her pain. That was another immensely painful yet healing moment that will remain engraved in my memory forever.

Louise wanted to continue with another scene, and I recall saying to her, "No more." I was emotionally saturated and felt that I had no more strength to continue. Gently, she encouraged me, and I found a renewed strength that I did not know I had hidden away somewhere. From there, we completed the circle of healing by re-enacting the first scene of writing my book again. Quite unexpectedly, I surprised myself as I rearranged the characters. This time I was my inner child, and I was writing my own book. I was holding onto the hands of my adult self on the one side and my anxiety on the other side, with my guardian angel touching me closely from behind. As I slowly let go of the hands of my adult self and my anxiety, Louise passed me a pen, saying that my hands were free to write whatever I wanted to write. I clearly recall starting to write, "I am OK" and then following Louise's guidance when she said, "I am broken ..." From there, the sentence finished itself for me, and I have kept this piece of writing up on my desk as I have continued writing this book. (See Figure 16.)

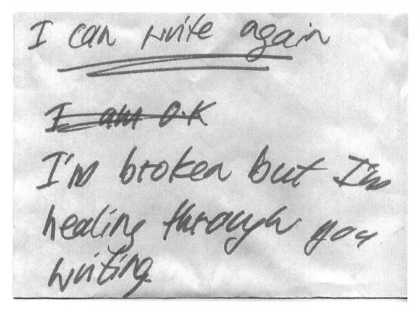

Figure 16
Personal writing on closure of psychodrama therapy session

I recall that, at the very end of the session, Louise suggested that I close my eyes and meditate, and reconnect with my guardian angel. During the brief meditation, the words of my guardian angel came to me, "I am your strength and your peace." A few days later, I typed these words on a card and placed it on my desk too, just below my desk lamp, where it is lit up as I continue my writing. (See Figure 17.)

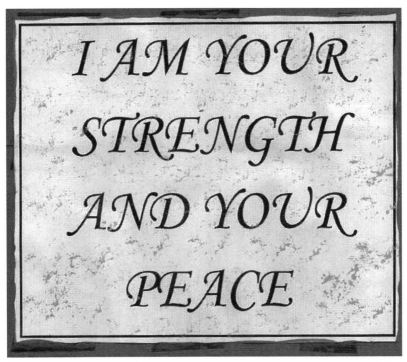

Figure 17
Desktop memoir of my guardian angel's message to me

In concluding this chapter, I would like to share with you an insight that came to me while writing it. As I wrote about the final scene in the psychodrama session, where my inner child became the writer of this book, I was transported back to a much earlier session with Louise. During my session on the Broken Child more than eighteen months previously, when using projective techniques and free association writing, I also wrote as my wise inner child to my adult self. I recall that, after I had shared the letter I had written with Louise, she had shared with me that my wise inner child, who was writing the letter, was really an expression of my soul. Louise's words were like a flash of lightning illuminating my experience of writing. It was my soul that had enabled me to flow so freely into the deep waters of my own grief and then return to the surface with relative peace and serenity. It continued facilitating this process in my psychodrama session, as well as throughout the process of writing this book. I am now able to reflect on my own healing progress since that session, and on how writing, in all of its different forms, has been an expression of my soul. The true significance of the sign on my desk, "I'm broken but I'm healing through you writing", has come alive for me now.

Thank you for journeying with me through this psychodrama experience. I hope that it was also helpful in reminding you that there is always a divine source of powerful healing and strength that we all can tap into at the most challenging times in our lives. I believe that sometimes a crisis presents itself to us to remind us to reconnect with our soul, in order to open the channel for us to, once again, access this eternal source of healing.

25

LOUISE'S PERSPECTIVE: THE GUARDIAN ANGEL PSYCHODRAMA

Louise

Psychodrama is a therapeutic method that uses drama in a therapeutic context in order to bring about healing. Any mental health care providers are able to learn the technique through a postgraduate course. One of the powerful elements of psychodrama is that the Then-and-There of the past or the future is re-created in the Here-and-Now. No changes can be made to our past, which is in the Then-and-There. However, changes can be made in the Here-and-Now. The therapist (in psychodrama terminology, the director) selects the most appropriate psychodrama techniques while the client (in psychodrama terminology, the protagonist) plays out their drama or situation. The different psychodrama techniques can be used for the client to: get insight from the other person's perspective (through the role reversal technique); vent all their feelings without holding back (through the empty chair technique); take a step back and review their own behaviour (through the mirroring technique);

or change their perspective of past events. As insight and change take place in the Here-and-Now, healing occurs. Psychodrama is an action-method that bypasses defence mechanisms and equips the protagonist to explore their inner and/or outer world, even if they don't have the words or thoughts properly formulated yet. This is the advantage that psychodrama has over narrative therapies, which require formulated thoughts and words. Psychodrama has the ability to tap into incredible sources of wisdom. It can be used in an individual setting or within a group setting. In psychodrama, when listening with the "ears of the soul", an astonishing number of sacred moments can be played out or acted out. Hazel's experience was no exception.

Hazel had started to write her book to tell her life story and, in the process, had taken out a lot of the old pictures she had drawn more than twenty years previously during a Holotropic Breathwork workshop. She had dusted them off and had taken a closer look. She phoned me and requested an urgent session to discuss the pictures. She sounded distraught, so we made an appointment at the earliest possible time.

When Hazel arrived, she stuffed the pictures into my hand without saying much. They were child-like drawings, drawn in wax crayons with bright colours. I looked at the pictures and must admit that I had to prevent myself from gasping. In one of the drawings, the hand of a female with long, manicured red nails was clearly visible. (See Figure 18.)

Figure 18
Female hand drawing

During our previous sessions, there had been times when Hazel and I had discussed the possibility that her mother had had some involvement in her sexual abuse, but nothing quite hit it home for me like this drawing. It upset me. Not wanting to put any words into Hazel's mouth, I tentatively asked, "What did you see that upset you?" She answered, "The female hands." I tried to explore with Hazel her thoughts and feelings around the "female hands", but she was quite adamant that she didn't want to deal with anything more around the abuse. She made it clear that she wanted to put the abuse behind her and focus on her future. She no longer wanted to give these "negative" pictures or ideas the time of day. Hazel did admit, though, that this new realisation had encroached on her writing and she felt stuck, unable to continue. Our session appeared to be suspended, due to Hazel's unwillingness to explore further and the strong defences she had put in place. A different approach was called for. With divine inspiration, I said to Hazel, "Then let's explore your inability to continue writing, within a vignette, i.e. a small/ short psychodrama."

As this activity seemed to be totally unrelated to the drawings, Hazel was keen to explore. We set up the first psychodrama scene, with her writing her book at her desk. Quickly, the psychodrama evolved with different characters: adult Hazel, inner child Hazel, and anxiety; and different scene settings followed. Yet we seemed to be dancing around an important issue, which at that stage was not named (or more accurately, could not be named). I then asked Hazel to identify someone who could help her get out of "being stuck" and she immediately said, "My guardian angel." Without wanting to return to Hazel's "mind space", we immediately brought her guardian angel into the drama and Hazel placed her guardian angel just behind her child. Through role reversal, Hazel moved between the roles of her guardian angel and her inner child as they were conversing. What ensued was incredibly powerful. It is said that experiencing goose-bumps when listening to or watching something is an indication of a spiritual moment; it is as if our souls are picking up on the importance of the experience or moment and then making it known to us. Hazel's inner child asked her guardian angel, "Why did you let this sexual abuse happen to me?" and, as Hazel swiftly moved into the role of her guardian angel, her body language changed, her tone of voice changed and the look in her eyes changed; there was incredible love for her inner child. As she was talking, goose-bumps ran up and down my arms and tears sprang to my eyes, as the conversation was seeped in a deeply profound and loving spiritual knowing. Her guardian angel answered, "I couldn't stop it, but I was there with you. I have always been there, and I have never left you, but you have forgotten about me. I see your pain and, although I could not stop what happened to you, I want to assure you that so much good will come from this. You will be able to transform your pain through your writing and then move on to healing others." The conversation continued with Hazel's guardian angel assuring her inner child of her support and inspiration during her life and her writing, although Hazel would need to ask for this help.

We completed the psychodrama with Hazel rearranging her previous writing scene. She changed the writing scene so that her inner child was now writing; it was no longer the adult Hazel who was writing. Next to her inner child was the adult Hazel on her right and her anxiety on her left. Her guardian angel was behind her, touching her inner child and giving her support. Hazel's level of anxiety had clearly subsided, and I could see that the psychodrama had touched her deeply.

We reflected on the psychodrama and looked at the significance and the implications. Over and above the obvious and profound conversation, Hazel realised that she did not have to do everything on her own, and that she could rely on support from her guardian angel. She committed to asking her guardian angel for help in the evenings before starting her writing. At that moment, one of us took the old wax drawings and pulled them closer. Lo and behold, on the drawing at the top of the pile, in her picture, was a distinct child-like drawing of Hazel's guardian angel. Then we took a closer look at the next picture and the next. Sure enough, despite the disturbing nature of the pictures themselves, the majority of her pictures had her guardian angel in them. Hazel's soul had known already and had left clues for Hazel's healing journey twenty years previously. How was it that we had never noticed before? It does appear that sometimes we need to believe before we are able to see with different eyes: ourselves, our world, and our reality. (See Figures 19 and 20.)

Figure 19
River of tears drawing

Figure 20
Guardian angel drawing

The story does not end there. Months later, Hazel was preparing to give a presentation on parts of her healing journey to a group of therapists at a workshop. She phoned me, scarcely able to contain her excitement: "Louise, you won't believe this. I found a drawing I made over twenty years ago, between all the drawings I brought with me for the psychodrama. I must have done this drawing at the same time as the others at the Holotropic Breathwork workshop, as it is dated the same as the others. Between all the drawings, somehow, we missed one. The drawing shows bright purple feathers, like the one found on the head of my guardian angel, on all my pictures." I was not sure of the significance. Hazel continued: "It's the same purple I used in my mandala at the second St. Raphael's Retreat and it has a strong resemblance to the two pictures I painted at the retreats, except that these purple feathers are bright and seen through an open window. They are floating; not confined. They are in the centre of the drawing and surrounded by the black and red that was in my paintings." (See Figure 21.)

Figure 21
Feathers in the centre drawing

Yes, it had been there all along; we just had not seen it. The English proverb, "There are none so blind as those who will not see", and Anaïs Nin's words, "We don't see things as they are; we see them as we are", come to mind. How much goodness and beauty we miss when the glasses through which we look at our world and ourselves are tainted by our own beliefs and perceptions!

26

THE HEALING POWER OF PRAYER

Louise

No book should discuss a spiritual journey without incorporating the spiritual practices of contemplation, meditation and prayer. All three are vitally important for deepening our spirituality, and each one has a unique role to play.

Contemplation is the practice of sitting quietly with a single word or concept in a totally non-judgemental way, and allowing the soul, not the mind, to engage with it. Our minds are inclined to make us feel safe by labelling and categorising information and by defining concepts or events in black-and-white terms. This is also known as dualistic thinking. During contemplation, we enable our thoughts to venture into more grey, non-dualistic thinking. Through contemplation, we can hold paradoxes and are even able to find a way to integrate what initially appeared to be opposing thoughts.

Centering Prayer is a method of contemplation.
We have included 2 videos as a free
gift for you which guides you
through a Centering Prayer exercise.
You can find it at www.TooCloseToRemember.com

Meditation focuses on the relaxation of the body and the mind – sitting within silence, in awareness. It allows us to hear our soul-whispers and to emerge into our consciousness or True Self, not trapped or tripped up by the world and our ego. Meditation allows us to go inward and, through meditation, to feel refreshed and invigorated. Interestingly enough, a study on the brain activity of Buddhist monks who have years of experience with meditating indicated that the vibrations of their brain activity occurred at the same frequency as that of the earth's crust. Take a moment to consider the implications of this.

Prayer can be defined as dialoguing with God. Through prayer, we aim to strengthen our relationship with God; we converse and spend time with Him. This differs from meditation and contemplation. Through meditation and contemplation, we can meditate and contemplate on our beliefs about God, but we can also focus on other concepts and beliefs that have nothing to do with our spiritual or religious beliefs about God. However, with prayer our sole focus is on God.

Recently, there have been a number of studies regarding the impact of prayer. One famous study by Dr Masaru Emoto involved praying over water droplets, which were then frozen. Dr Emoto took three sets of water droplets and exposed them to different stimuli. He treated the first set of droplets with aggression; he screamed at them and said abusive things to them. To the second set of droplets, he said kind, positive and uplifting words. Lastly, he prayed over the third group of water droplets. All three sets of water droplets were then frozen. Once they were frozen, Dr Emoto viewed the water crystals in the droplets under a microscope. The patterns of the crystals that the water droplets froze into were markedly different. The first group of crystals had sharp, jagged points, and their patterns were sharp and haphazard. The second group of water crystals displayed softer, prettier patterns. The last group of crystals had patterns that were flowery and exquisitely beautiful; considerably different from the other two groups.

In another research project, scientists used five different trays of bean sprouts. In workshops all over the world, the presenter would ask the audience she addressed to randomly select one of the trays and to spend some time, then and there, to pray for that selected tray of bean sprouts to grow. The scientists would then monitor the growth of the bean sprouts in all the trays and compare them to one another and to the tray selected by the audience. The research was conducted in the USA and also as far afield as Australia. Yet the results were significant, with some bean sprouts growing twice as much when prayed for than the bean sprouts in the other trays that had not been prayed for. These studies show that there is still much that we cannot explain about prayer when viewed or defined only by the mind or science.

Coming back to Hazel's journey, we notice two things. Firstly, in Hazel's dialogue with her anxiety, her soul encouraged her to meditate, to become calm and centred, and to not be overwhelmed by the world. Because Hazel started the journey as an esoteric, I did not want to convert her to my Christian beliefs; that was never the aim of the journey. I found myself substituting the concept of prayer with meditation. When I wanted to encourage her to pray, I would consciously encourage her to meditate.

This brings me to the second observation. Hazel's journey with Joshua brought her to an NG (Dutch Reformed) dominee (pastor) who has been gifted with the gift of healing. As he does not work with young children, he prayed over Hazel and instructed her on how and when to pray over her son. She described her experience of being prayed over by the dominee as a warm, pins-and-needles-like sensation flowing over her. When she prayed over her son while he was sleeping, she experienced the same sensation flowing out of her, through her arm, into her son. Until that point, her son had shown minimal progress in spite of receiving some intense play therapy, over a period of two years, from one of the country's best play therapists specialising in sexually abused victims and perpetrators. After Hazel started praying for her son, he started to heal. What do we make of all of this?

Christians lay their hands on and pray for people with all types of illnesses, who are then instantly healed. What is particularly evident in the Bible is that everyone who asked for healing from Jesus was healed. Healing was one of His core ministries. Yet, He didn't cure everyone in the same way. One man had to go and wash himself in a pool; for another, Jesus made a paste from spittle and mud, and placed the paste on the man's eyes; a woman who had severe haemorrhaging just needed to touch Jesus' cloak to be healed; another man was healed by having his sins forgiven; while a centurion was healed when he asked Jesus just to say the "word". I believe that this reflects the spiritual truth that Jesus does not heal us all in the same way, because we are all so different in our makeup and beliefs. Perhaps the method of healing is part of the healing in itself.

What I have come to realise through this journey is that we should indeed be engaging in all three practices (contemplation, meditation and prayer) to deepen our spirituality. I am sure that these practices are not exclusive and that there are other useful spiritual practices as well. Each of these three practices has a unique value and a unique aim, and they enhance each other. Prayer is not synonymous with meditation. Of particular interest in the Bible, is the occasion when Jesus asked a man, "Do you want to be healed?", to which the man answered, "Of course I want to be healed"; and only then did Jesus heal him. I do believe that when people have been chronically ill for a lengthy period, the idea of being healed can be frightening. Perhaps that is why we need to ask to be healed; to pray to God for healing. With the praying, comes the belief that we will be healed; that God wants us to be healed.

Do I think Joshua could have been healed just through prayer? Yes, I do believe that nothing is impossible for God, and that God could have healed him instantly if He so chose. Do I believe there is only one way of healing? No. I believe that God uses doctors, psychologists, medicine, therapists, prayer, etc. to heal. One has only to have journeyed with Hazel to realise how many people, even to this point, have been touched and affected by her and Joshua's journey. These include her immediate family, her extended family, me, the play therapist, Joshua's remarkable preschool teacher, and the therapists who have heard Hazel's story. I also have no doubt that many more people will be touched in the future. If God had healed Joshua instantly, what would be the point of gifting the dominee with healing, as we would only need God for our healing? Would Hazel have been able to come to a place of forgiveness of her mother at the time when she most needed to forgive her? We are inextricably linked to each other as spiritual beings, and others' stories form important parts of our stories of being human and of upliftment. Our interconnectedness is a profoundly beautiful part of our human experience – we all have different gifts, strengths, characteristics and experiences (the good and the tough parts) that form the tapestry of a meaningful, purpose-driven life.

READER'S REFLECTION:

Take the time to reflect on your thoughts and beliefs surrounding prayer. Take a moment to identify one experience or event you have been through that has been particularly tough for you. Now take a closer look and see how many people have formed part of your story. For now, it is not necessary to judge or categorise them as being "good / right" or "bad / wrong" – just view them as being part of your journey; look for the interconnectedness.

27

THE AFTERMATH

Hazel

"Be still and know that I am God" (Psalm 46:10)

On our return journey after the confrontation, I once again felt drawn to visit the little chapel in Matjiesfontein at the Lord Milner Hotel. Being aware that I had carried through the answer given to me there only three days previously, I wanted to reconnect with the spiritual strength that I had found there.

My mind was relatively calm and at peace as I moved to sit down in a chair. Like a bolt of lightning from heaven, the words "Be still and know that I am God" came to me before I had even sat down. The words were crystal clear and had come to me prior to any attempt to meditate or clear my mind. As I sat down, I focused on my breath, and it was as if I was breathing these words into my whole being. I tried to clear a space from these words, to see if anything else might come to me. The same words repeated themselves over and over again. I could never have surmised the depth of the significance of this message for me at the time. However, I knew that the message needed to become the very air that I breathed in, for what lay ahead of me in the next stage of my journey.

It was less than a week after returning from the confrontation that Joshua was suspended from preschool for inappropriate sexual behaviour. From feeling emotionally saturated yet somehow still coping and being reasonably stable in myself, I was thrown into a deep pit of depression, and felt as if I was shutting down on all levels. It became a big battle for me to get out of bed and to just get through each day. I recall receiving a WhatsApp message from my niece during that time, with the news that my father had been knocked over by a car and was in hospital. I didn't think too much of it at the time; being quite numb to everything that was going on around me, I paid little attention to it.

Approximately a month after that, my mother started sending me countless emails, in which she viciously attacked and blamed me for the accident that had happened, saying that it was my fault entirely, due to the stress that I had caused my father by my accusation. I was in no state to deal with her unending attacks on me, and Louise stepped in and answered some of the e-mails on my behalf. I felt as if I was drowning in the depths of an ocean of numbed pain at the time, having been hit by two massive tidal waves within days of each other. As I write this now, I realise the extent to which Louise so freely and unconditionally extended God's grace to me at that time, and I am at a loss for words in my gratitude to her for this.

One of my clearest memories of that time is of being at Mark's house, finally finding a few hours of peace to myself, and reading Eckhart Tolle's book *Stillness Speaks*. Mark had kindly taken Joshua out for trampolining and it was the first bit of solitude I had had in what seemed like a lifetime since Joshua's suspension from preschool. I felt as if I was stopping to drink at an oasis in the desert. As I drank in the words of the book, they slowly began to quench my desperate thirst for some peace of mind and stillness. Feeling a space clearing within me, I wished that I could continue drinking in the words, but I needed to start getting dinner ready. While in the kitchen, my cell phone rang twice from an unknown number. I don't usually answer these calls, but on the third call I decided to take the call. It was from the clinical psychologist working at the hospital where my father was in the rehabilitation ward at that time. After having to take an initial deep breath, I was fortunately in a relatively calm frame of mind while she told me that it was the psychiatrist's opinion that my father's accident could possibly have been a suicide attempt. The world stood still around me as she then followed this news with, "Your father would really like to see you as soon as possible to try to resolve this." Everything felt somewhat unreal, as if I was in a dream in which I was aware that I was dreaming – with only a blurry haze defining the boundary between reality and the dream. The child in me wanted to trust that there was now some hope of reconciliation and that my father would openly apologise to me. The adult in me quickly drowned out my child's voice with total mistrust and cynicism, and I was once again on a battlefield. However, in the midst of this battle, I found a safe space from which I could speak from my heart, and I told the psychologist that I would definitely consider coming to see my father, but that I would need a little time to sort out my plans. Shortly after our conversation ended, Mark and Joshua arrived back home, and I was thrown back into the here-and-now of organising dinner. Surprisingly, the earth had not opened up completely beneath me, but had only cracked slightly, and I was able to jump back towards the dinner table without falling into the crack. I found a moment to tell Mark the news and was somewhat surprised by his response. He didn't seem too surprised or shocked, and we talked about whether or not I should go to see my father. I started making plans, liaising with my father through the psychologist. My plans became thwarted by my mother's interference as an old, familiar family pattern re-emerged – she was once again controlling my father; he was the puppet on her string.

My mind swam in an ocean of guilt and regret for having confronted my father with the accusation that he had sexually abused me. Although my head was still just above the water level, I felt as if I was starting to drown. My mind was winning the battle with my heart as it started dragging me under this sea of guilt and regret, fuelled by my mother's continual emotional attacks on me. Finally, Louise returned from a trip to the Camino in Spain and, once again, I realised that I had managed to get through confronting my father without her being there at the time. I had also managed to cope with finding the letter that I had written to him more than twenty years ago, finally confirming my opinion that it could have been him who had sexually abused me. Looking back now, I realise that Louise's relatively long period of absence during two of the most critical and challenging points in my healing journey held a valuable lesson for me – I was able to heal myself by opening my soul's channel to a greater source of divine healing and strength.

I felt responsible for my father's possible suicide attempt and wanted to rescue him from it, because I felt that it was my fault. I knew that territory of mine so well, and yet was struggling to see it once again for what it was – my re-emerging pattern of self-blame. I saw a glimmer of light and started to gain a slightly new perspective after further counselling with Louise – my father needed to go on the journey through his own pain and face himself and the consequences of what had happened to me. I also needed time to heal further before making a decision about whether to see him again, and when. Time would be a healer, and right then we could not put any definite time limit on the healing process. Gradually, over the next few months, the battle between my mind and my heart started to find its own resolution. The process was so slow that I hardly noticed the changes until I started to feel "lighter" again. Retrospectively, I now realise that the "lighter" feeling had its source in listening to the whispering voice of my soul. I slowly started to embrace a new perspective – it was not my fault, but rather his chosen journey. I was moving towards becoming ready to make contact with my parents again, having made contact with my soul.

At the same time, I started to gain some further insight into my mother's deep state of woundedness, as the content of her emails started to become more extreme in her attacks on me.

According to her, not only was I "very sick" and in desperate need of "treatment" to become "better", but I was also "psychotic". There were strong implications that Louise had put these ideas into my mind, as had the psychologists that I had seen in the past. I felt, in a sense, some level of relief, as this enabled me to gain perspective from a distance. It was what I needed to continue to break free from the residue of my lingering guilt.

My siblings' responses to my accusation against my father had shown some striking similarities, as well as differences. Perhaps what disturbed and saddened me the most was that two of my brothers, Mark and Derrick, asked me whether I thought that it could have been anything that they had done to me that was now causing this trauma. I felt very upset that they could be blaming themselves for this and, as much as I assured them that this was most definitely not the case, I felt stunned at the same initial response from both of them. Could it be because they would rather blame themselves than have to confront the possibility of their father being responsible? Was it an emotionally impossible territory for them to move into?

I recall being very upset after reading my eldest brother Thomas's email response to the email I had written, outlining how I had reached certainty in my opinion that my father had sexually abused me. It had taken me a few evenings to compile my email to him, which was a number of pages in length. He responded with a few lines stating that, given the information that I had sent to him, he was not convinced either way. He was remaining neutral in that he chose not to say whether or not he believed that it had happened. He thought that there was simply not enough evidence for him to prove, beyond any doubt, that my father had sexually abused me. It wasn't so much the relatively "clinical" nature of his response that upset me; after all, this had always been his character. Rather, I was left feeling that I had finally found the courage to pour out my heart and soul to him, only to receive such a short response; something that would have taken him perhaps five minutes to write. Also, he had not phoned me to talk about the matter – instead, he had just sent an email. It felt to me like this increased the distance that lay between us. We had been living at opposite ends of the planet for about ten years and had seen each other only twice in that time. Had time and space created such a distance between us that the matter of my abuse was simply not something he was willing to put much time or energy into? I felt deeply saddened, as if I had completely lost whatever loose emotional bond had existed between us. I felt both anger towards him and a sense of rejection from him, not because he did not believe me, but rather because of his apparent lack of empathy and time given to me after what I had been through. However, in time, I slowly came to realise that my siblings' responses told me more about where they were in their own personal relationships with my parents, and their resulting processing of this, rather than being a reflection of their personal feelings towards me. This insight made it a lot easier for me to not take their responses so personally. By remaining neutral, they were able to remain in safer territory themselves, emotionally, while trying to process the enormity of the matter. It took me more than twenty years to be able to confront and finally process things emotionally. Only after a very long period of fluctuating anxiety, depression and denial did I shift towards a neutral attitude. (Maybe I was abused by my father, maybe I wasn't – I don't have enough evidence.) Then, only much later, I finally moved into anger, intense and overwhelming grief, and finally acceptance of my opinion that my father was responsible for my sexual abuse. How could I expect anything different from my brothers? They were on a similar journey to mine – he still remains their father, regardless of anything else in the family history. Later, Thomas had a change in opinion after I sent him the CD recording of my confrontation with my father. It seemed to be more convincing for him and, as a result, he acknowledged that it appeared that my father may indeed have sexually abused me. Thomas also stated that he was with me on the matter.

I also recall that, at an earlier stage, there had been a major conflict between Mark and Thomas when I had initially started dealing with the trauma. Mark and Derrick had asked Thomas whether he would be willing to help finance some therapy with a clinical psychologist for me, and Thomas had not been willing to contribute. At some level, I felt that I was not only at the centre of a massive family conflict, but that I was also the cause of it. My head and my heart were back on the battlefield – my head told me that it was my fault, but my heart told me that I couldn't blame myself.

My parents desperately wanted me to go to see them and their psychologist. Initially, as a compromise, I agreed to speak to them on Skype with Louise, to see whether we could come to any kind of resolution. I recall clearly that, just before the conversation started, Louise suggested that we close our eyes, meditate briefly, and ask for strength and guidance. I felt at peace in that moment, knowing that, once again, we could access divine guidance and strength. My parents would not agree to accept our differences of opinion on the "truth", or to come to a compromise in accepting that our "truths" are different. They insisted on an apology from me for my "false accusation", and that was something that I was not prepared to offer. We had come to a complete "stalemate" situation. Once again, while talking to them, I experienced a strong sense of inner strength coming to me from a greater divine source, enabling me to remain calm, focused, and relatively non-defensive and non-reactive. I managed to remain centred in myself, which must have been divinely inspired, as it had been an immensely challenging conversation, with much potential for immense conflict between us. Sadly, our discussion confirmed for me that reconciliation was probably never going to be possible – I needed to reconcile and make peace within myself.

I remember meeting with Louise around that time and talking to her about her decision to no longer have any direct communication with my mother because my mother had threatened a court case and Louise felt that she needed to withdraw from the situation. She felt professionally vulnerable, as the techniques she used were ground-breaking but would not necessarily be supported by fellow colleagues or by her professional body. I felt my all-too-familiar sense of guilt; that this was somehow my fault.

Louise had offered me her professional support unconditionally through such a traumatic experience and now, as a result, she was left questioning stepping outside her professional boundaries. I felt like I wanted to protect her. At the same time, I started to wonder whether this could possibly be the beginning of a whole new, much more challenging journey, just at a time when I thought I had come through the worst. I felt that I could never find the strength for that, and I started to lose faith in what I had always known – that there is always a divine purpose for our pain.

As time went by after our Skype conversation, there appeared to be a possibility that my father would take me to court for a false accusation of sexual abuse. This was also strongly implied in some of my parents' email conversations with me, as well as in my parents' attempts to gather evidence by contacting my past psychologists and by requesting a current clinical psychologist's report. I recall feeling torn on the issue of whether or not to see an independent clinical psychologist to get the requested report for my parents. On the one hand, it seemed to be a reasonable request, given my accusation and the fact that I had no conscious memory of my abuse. My mind was telling me to go ahead and see the psychologist for their sake and also for my own sense of personal integrity – the need to provide further evidence and justification for my accusation. On the other hand, I knew what the outcome of that would be: a report stating the high proba-bility of my accusation being true, based on the psychologist's assessment. At the end of the day, nothing could be proven with a hundred percent certainty, as there was no remaining physical evidence or witness of my abuse, and there never would be. Having put an awful lot of time and energy into the process, we would simply be back where we had started; my parents would deny any responsibility. I wanted to move forward with my life, directing my energy into writing this book and looking towards the future. However, I still felt a sense of guilt at the need to provide more evidence through a psychologist's report. Initially, I did not agree to getting a current psychologist's report. However, at a later stage, I finally agreed to getting the psychologist's report, just before things took a very different turn.

I remember, as if it were yesterday, how the ground shifted beneath me again when I responded to my father's request on my cell phone. He wanted me to suggest a way forward, given that he would not acknowledge responsibility for something that he felt he was not responsible for. I had had enough of going around in endless circles with the "nice" approach, and my anger had resurfaced. I suggested that he go for a polygraph test. For a while there was no response at all, until I received an email stating, amongst other things, that he would not put himself through that amount of stress, and that the results of a polygraph test would be invalid, as they could not stand as evidence in a court of law. At that stage, his response was exactly what I had expected, and only confirmed what I had confronted him with. Little did I know what was still to come.

A few months later, I received a message stating that a poly-graph test had been arranged for my father, who had agreed to be tested, and that the tester would be in contact with me soon, with some questions. I was somewhat surprised at the turnaround, but still felt relatively calm within myself. I spoke to the tester, who asked me about the nature of the accusation and how I defined sexual abuse. I really struggled to make sense of it all when the tester told me that my mother was demanding the test, due to me having accused my father of raping me. Despite knowing that this was not the exact accusation that I had made, I once again felt like I was moving back into a whirlwind. I was starting to lose stillness at my centre and was once again being blown by the storm towards its outer edges.

The results of the test were positive, in favour of my father. The ground beneath me suddenly collapsed as I started falling into the massive dark cave it had opened up beneath me. I had absolutely no means of making sense of the result, and I have to admit that I was completely dumbfounded by it at the time. Thomas was intensely angry at me, because I refused to apolo-gise sincerely to my father and I said that I did not accept the validity of the test result, although I was unable to clearly justify my specific reasons at that stage. Thomas immediately told my father that he was pleased for him about the result of the test. He also made it quite clear to me that he did not think that I needed any further therapy. He told my siblings that too and encouraged them not to offer any financial help in that respect, if requested. He stated that if I chose to pursue any more therapy, it would need to be at my own expense. His response was immediate and very decisive, with no further questions asked – it was final, and we would simply have to agree to disagree. Mark, having been told that my mother had requested the test, saying that I had accused my father of raping me, now seemed to think that it was her strategy to keep herself free of blame. He thought that she knew that she had also played a role in my abuse and that, in fact, my father had possibly not committed the act of raping me as such. The few dreams of mine that had implied my mother's collaboration in my abuse, as well as the picture I had drawn of female hands sexually abusing a young child, all seemed to come flooding back to me. It would also explain why my parents had turned around from their initial response of refusing to do the polygraph test. Mark also raised new questions – Had I somehow projected this onto my father? Was there a possibility that my father had been actively involved in some way, without necessarily being the perpetrator of my abuse, but that the perpetrator had rather been my mother or someone else?

I remember going to talk to Louise at that time, and her asking me how I was. I answered, saying that I didn't know how I was feeling; there was just a mass of confusion. I shared with her that, at that point, I felt unable to continue writing, as I was once again swimming in a sea of self-doubt – not quite drowning; just managing to stay afloat somehow, but also feeling that a deep depression was threatening to sink me. I needed to feel able to swim in order to be able to write again. We talked at length and, somehow, it feels as if that conversation took place yesterday. At first, Louise shared with me the need to find a way to hold onto this paradox – that it is possible to hold both of these seemingly opposite "truths" simultaneously (the results of the polygraph test, and my absolute sense of knowing that my father had sexually abused me despite the lack of a conscious memory of it). These appeared to be in direct opposition to each other and there was not a specific resolution at that point in time. However, I needed to try to hold onto the possibility that these two "opposites" could co-exist, and that a resolution would be revealed in time. Secondly, Louise shared the importance of "process" – that is, continuing with the process of writing, despite my self-doubt at that stage. I did not necessarily need to engage in direct battle with my self-doubt, but I needed to accept it as being part of my journey at that point. I needed to try not to become completely overwhelmed by it through identifying with it completely. From the space within which the paradox was held, my healing journey and writing would continue.

Louise had more faith in me than I had in myself at that tremendously challenging time, and I want to thank her for that as I write these words. My tears are starting to well up now as I look back on how I have continued to heal since the time during which she shared these pearls of wisdom with me.

As I drove home after meeting with Louise, my head and heart tried to grasp what she had shared with me, but with very little success. It was perhaps the first time that I felt unable to try to reach far beyond myself to touch the heart of what she had said. As soon as I briefly made contact with it, it slipped through my hands again, leaving me wondering whether, at that point, we were somehow on different wavelengths, and feeling unsure of whether our waves could re-connect.

Over the next few weeks, I continued to fight an enormous battle with myself, trying to get to my writing again. Finally, I managed to let go of my personal expectations of what needed to happen when I tried to write again – I decided that if I wrote nothing at all, that would be fine, as long as I tried to make a start again, even if that meant only opening up my computer with the intention of writing. Rather than continuing with the chapter that I had been writing, I chose to start on an easier chapter:

"Finding Purpose through Pain". The old familiar writer's block came pounding loudly at my door again, but the door remained firmly locked for quite some time. It was only after about the third attempt at writing again that the door started to open. As it opened, my depression started to lift, and I began to feel a sense of vitality within me again. It was the simple step-by-step physical process of sitting down and starting to write that had enabled me to release the lock on the door to my writing again – the door of my inner healer.

A few days after the polygraph test results were revealed, a totally unexpected opportunity arose for me to travel with Karen, Mark's girlfriend, and her children up to visit Derrick. This provided me with a much-needed opportunity to see my father in person again. It was a gift sent from heaven, as I really needed to see him myself to discuss with him my response to the polygraph test results. However, as much as I knew that I needed to grasp the opportunity with both hands, I was still unsure as to exactly what I would say to him. I knew what I wanted to say, but I couldn't find the words to express it. I recall vividly now my conversation with Karen after all the children in the back seat had finally fallen asleep. When she helped me find the words I needed, I was finally at peace with what was to come the next day.

On meeting my father again, I felt anxious, but this time my anxiety did not threaten to overwhelm me. Rather, like an old friend, it was just knocking on the door quite firmly, wanting to come into my home. I opened the door and allowed it to take a seat beside me, rather than inside me. As my father approached the table where I was sitting at the restaurant, I saw him firstly as a sad, fragile old man, and secondly as my father. I stood up, walked towards him and gave him a hug. At that moment, I felt no sense of confusion or anger, only an inexplicable sense of relief.

My father shared with me that he could not remember ever having sexually abused me and that this must mean that he did not do it. Despite it being such a long time ago, he was sure that the significance of something like that would be engraved in his memory if he had done that to me. As his eyes met mine, I felt confused again – was he trying to be honest with me as he looked directly into my eyes? While we spoke, I held onto my sense of truth and said that I was no longer one hundred percent certain whether he was, or was not, the person who had sexually abused me. Due to the fact that I had no absolute certainty either way, I was therefore still not willing to either apologise or to retract my accusation, despite the test results. I could only withdraw my accusation and apologise if I had full certainty that he was not my abuser. At that stage, I did not have that certainty. I asked him whether, hypothetically assuming that he was not responsible for having sexually abused me, he would be able to help me identify who had abused me and whether he knew of anyone else who might have done it. He answered in one short word, "No". The silence that followed his single-word answer was deafening. I sat with the silence for what felt like an eternity before asking him whether he was sure, to which he replied with one more word, "Yes". At the time, I could not quite define what the deafening noise in the silence meant. Subsequently, I have thought about it in terms of how I would respond if it was my own child making such an accusation against me. I realised that perhaps I might be a bit angry at first at a false accusation. However, if they then asked me to help them find out who it may have been if it wasn't me, I would then try my utmost best to help them find out who it could have been, out of love and concern for my child. So, what did this mean? Did it speak of guilt? I then went on to let my father know that I suspected that my mother had also been involved in my sexual abuse, and I explained my reasons for this. (On our first confrontation, my father had chosen to ask me whether my accusation was directed only at him or at my mother as well. After that confrontation, my mother had asked me who in the family knew about the abuse, how much they knew, and for how long they had known. She had also emphatically stated that she wanted me to know that she knew absolutely nothing about it, but at the same time she had expressed no empathy for what I had been through.) My father responded, warning me that I was moving into "dangerous territory", but also stating that he would not stand in my way if I chose to confront my mother. Our conversation started to go around in circles as we repeated our points of view, and soon after that, my mother came to join us. Initially, I had no intention of speaking to her about my suspicions of her involvement in my abuse. However, as I was unable to make contact with Derrick, who was coming to pick me up, I chose to ask her whether she could perhaps help me to identify who it was that had sexually abused me, assuming that it was not my father. For the first time since my initial accusation, she went on at great length, identifying all potential suspects, and literally finished my sentence for me when I reflected that these had all been times when I had not been staying at home. I clearly remember the feelings I experienced when she took the words out of my mouth, saying, "... when you had not been at home." She continued by saying that it must have happened when I was away from home, as the test results affirm that my father was not responsible. My intuition told me that she was hiding herself in the picture – this was not a feeling but rather a deep sense of knowing. This was further confirmed for me by her many ongoing e-mail messages offering me endless possibilities of people who could have been the perpetrators, all of whom were not relatives and lived outside of the family home. Her responses, at that stage, were simply too many and too late. They left me highly suspicious as to the reasons why she had chosen to share only one of the possibilities with me before that point; a possibility that was contradictory to what she was saying now. (She had mentioned my foster mother in the past, who, ironically, she now claimed could not have been responsible for abusing me, because she would have been properly referenced by the Child Welfare Department.)

As we politely said goodbye, I was left with one further answer confirmed and one question remaining. My mother knew exactly what had happened to me and had been at the very least responsible for collaborating with the abuser, if not having sexually abused me herself. My father might possibly have lost his memory of what had happened; however, if he was personally responsible for sexually abusing me, surely, he would remember that. So, was he lying to me or could it possibly mean that he was not personally responsible for sexually abusing me? I still struggled with these questions but, somehow, I knew that I needed to be able to continue to hold the paradox as I continued on my journey.

Writing about this now is enabling me to gain a new perspective on my own healing, as well as on the personal insights I gained between the two times I met with my father; a period of about ten months. I can now see how I had managed my anxiety by befriending it to a certain extent, and that it no longer held the same power over me. Upon deeper reflection, I also now see parallels in my father's responses on both occasions – he did not once look me in the eyes and directly deny ever having sexually abused me. (On the first occasion, he had said that if he could not remember specific details, that did not necessarily mean that it did or did not happen. On the second occasion, he had said that the fact that he could not remember it must mean that it did not happen.) Furthermore, he expressed very little anger towards me, despite the nature of my accusation and my refusal to accept the validity of the results of the polygraph test. I also felt that he expressed virtually no sense of genuine empathy or concern for what I had been through (assuming he was not responsible for it). This manifested in a complete lack of willingness to even attempt to help me find the person responsible for the abuse. However, I still struggled to make sense of the meaning and/or significance of these emerging parallels.

Quite some time after I had been up to speak to my father again, Mark told me about a meeting that he had had with my father. Their conversation had quickly turned to my accusation against my father as my father tried to convince Mark that he was definitely not responsible for my abuse and that my accusation had been false. Mark had not given my father the answers that he had been hoping to hear by agreeing with him. Towards the end of the conversation, Mark had told them that he had absolutely no uncertainty that my mother and my father both knew exactly what had happened to me in my sexual abuse and that they knew who had been responsible for it. Mark had closed the conversation by stating that he knew that they were both choosing to remain silent on what they knew. This statement had been followed by complete silence from both my mother and father.

When Mark told me about this meeting, I found further confirmation in what my soul already knew – that both of my parents were guilty with regard to my sexual abuse, although I could not prove this with 100% certainty. Despite not knowing specific facts about exactly what their role was in my abuse, I was healing and finding my peace.

As time passed, I became more aware of something that had been at the back of my mind since the polygraph test. We knew a leading polygraph test expert who lived in the same town, and I had mentioned (to both Louise and my husband) the possibility of getting a second opinion on the test results from him, although I had never followed up on it. This was an ideal opportunity to get a second professional opinion from someone who had been in the field for twenty-six years and whose internationally renowned credentials, experience and expertise could be highly valuable to me in this crisis. So why had I not approached him soon after the test? I was hesitant to share my deeply personal story with someone who had been an acquaintance a few years previously, but was this my primary reason for not taking the opportunity? To tell you the honest truth, I was also genuinely frightened of the possible result of consulting him. What if he confirmed that the test was indeed comprehensive, and the results valid? Where would that leave me? How would I ever make peace with my family and with myself? I just didn't know whether I had the strength to face that.

I postponed getting a second opinion until such time that I had reached the point of writing this chapter in the book. I somehow just couldn't find the strength to start the chapter, knowing the emotional challenges it would bring. I spoke to Louise and we decided to start on editing some of the first few chapters and then come back to this one at a later stage; perhaps when I felt more ready for it, having had a break on an emotional level. As time went on, I decided to ask Louise to help me with a skeleton framework for this chapter, thinking that it might help me get started on it. As we approached the end of discussing the framework, I commented that the next natural step at that stage would be for me to approach the polygraph expert to discuss the test results. We both agreed that that was where this chapter needed to find its ending, whatever that ending might entail. In a synchronistic way, as I now peer over at the paper on which this chapter's framework was written, I notice that the meeting with the polygraph tester is listed right at the bottom of the third and final page, leaving no more space for anything further. Intuitively, I knew that I was going to contact the polygraph expert once I had reached this point in writing the chapter, rather than before then, and that is exactly what I did. It was as if the process of writing was enabling me to become emotionally ready to meet with the polygraph expert and to deal with whatever the result of our meeting would be.

Laughing, I said to Louise while we waited at the front gate of the polygraph expert's house, "No mention of the soul here please, this is as clinical as it gets!" With regard to the actual test results, his feedback was that the report was unusually short and brief; the two questions asked to elicit a response were not well structured; and standard industry practice required that a third question be asked. Furthermore, the pretest questions should have been included in the report, together with medical information on my father, including what medication he was using at the time of the test. The report from my father's polygraph test results was a "social report" rather than a fully comprehensive polygraph test report and, for the moment, the polygraph expert regarded the results to be invalid, and he stated that further testing was required. He recommended and offered a free re-test of my father and myself, if my father would come to the town where we lived. Alternatively, he could find an examiner to do a re-test for R500. I recalled at this point that the polygraph tester who had tested my father had initially said to me that he was unable to do a full test but rather needed to do an "interview" due to the fact that there was no hard, factual evidence for the accusation. Despite that, due to my mother's ongoing request for the test, he had carried out the test. There now seemed to be some parallels emerging in what the two polygraph testers had told me, but I could not quite put my finger on them at the time.

The polygraph expert then went on to ask me some questions about how the polygraph test had come about and, more specifically, how my father had responded to me when I was with him and made the accusation against him. The expert's opinion was that the fact that my father had not once directly denied my accusation to me, was an indication of guilt. We went on to ask the expert about how the possible loss of memory due to old age could influence the test results and/or a subject's memory of an experience like that. There was a bit of a twist in the tale when he then asked about my father's current state of health – was he still able to get himself out of bed and/or dress himself? When I replied positively to this, the expert replied that he was sure that my father would remember if he had done that to me. The expert had tested sexual offenders in the past and, in his experience, their memory did not fail them with regard to that type of immensely significant experience, even over long periods of time. In fact, the evidence shows that memories of that type of experience tend to remain much clearer than other memories over the same period of time. The exception was in the case of severe and advanced failing health. At that stage, I started believing that my father must have been untruthful when he said that he could not remember ever having abused me.

It was a fairly short meeting (about forty- five minutes at the most), but in that short space of time, I had found my final peace and healing. There was no paradox to hold anymore. As I stepped into the car, I felt a little tearful. A wave of absolute relief washed over me while I was driving home a little later, and my tears started to flow.

There were many more challenges within the family after this, with Thomas gaining a different polygraph expert's opinion about the validity of the report on my father's test. That expert was of the opinion that the test results were valid. Thomas also wanted me to go for a polygraph test myself and he wanted my father to be re-tested. Although I still struggled with these pressures and decisions, I started to make my peace with not continuing the testing, despite others' opinions.

A short while after my meeting with the polygraph tester, I sent Louise a WhatsApp message: "This is where one journey ends, and another begins. Thank you for holding my hand on the journey (and carrying me at times). Our book will finish soon, or our part in it, and it will carry others through their pain too ..." As I now read this on my cell phone screen and type it on my keyboard, it confirms my decision to let this book find its natural ending here. This is a place of peace where I know beyond any doubt that I can trust the voice of my soul – the channel to my guardian angel and a greater source of divine wisdom and healing.

I hope that, as you travel on your journey through your own pain, my experiences shared with you here may offer you strength to trust your own inner wisdom when you feel like everything around you is making you lose faith in yourself. Try not to cave in on yourself when nothing makes sense anymore. For now, you may need to hold onto a paradox so that you can continue on your healing journey. The answers that you need, in order to find your peace and resolve your paradox, will be revealed to you in time.

28

THE AFTERMATH: HOLDING PARADOXES AND TRANSFORMATION

Louise

In April 2017, my husband and I left for Spain to walk the Santiago de Compostela, also known as the Camino Pilgrimage. It had been at the top of my bucket list for almost twenty years and, since the children had all left home to study at the beginning of 2017, it was the ideal time for us to take seven weeks off to walk the Camino. I felt assured that Hazel was doing well; that we had reached a resting place in treatment. Hazel had said that she was going to visit her brother for Easter and did not feel ready to confront her father. All work aspects were taken care of, with back-ups in place and an automatic out-of-office reply set on my email. To avoid having to look at non-urgent or non-work-related emails while on the Camino, I decided to set up a new email account for use on the pilgrimage. Only close friends and family had the address for the e-mail account on which we decided to correspond once a week, on Sundays, to touch base and to reflect on our journey.

Upon opening my emails on the second Sunday, I found one from an unknown address. I was totally taken aback and puzzled, and then opened the email. It was from Hazel's mother, telling me that I must please help urgently because Hazel had accused her father of the most terrible things. The email was so unexpected that I became overwhelmed with numerous thoughts and feelings. So, Hazel did confront her father? How did her mother get my email address? What bad timing! What could I do now, thousands of kilometres away, when I wasn't going to be back for another five weeks? I was really annoyed at having my privacy encroached upon, and felt even more irritated that, after having waited twenty years to do the pilgrimage that held out the promise of spiritual insight and discernment, I was forced to sort out a crisis for other people. There was another dark element in all of it: Hazel's mother had approached all her colleagues and acquaintances, proclaiming to the world "what Hazel had done", in an attempt to get people on her side. Something so traumatic and private, she had openly blasted to anyone who would hear and from whom she could get sympathy. There was no regard or concern for her daughter's pain, nor any respect for her experience. To Hazel's mother, it was about being right. For a period of almost eighteen months, she continuously badgered Hazel to apologise. Please don't misunderstand. I have no idea what it must be like for a daughter to confront her father about sexual abuse and for his wife to be a witness. Not for one moment could I even imagine what Hazel's mother must have been going through. Only in my imagination do I believe that my reaction would have been very different. I admit that, as much as I tried, I could not get rid of the nagging insinuations from Hazel's letters and dreams that somehow her mother had not only known about the abuse, but had possibly even played some part in it. Neither could I ignore the history of the active part she played in the sexual abuse of Hazel's brother, Mark.

Hazel's mother wouldn't respect any boundaries, hence the emails (not only those sent while I was on my pilgrimage, but also numerous others sent afterwards) and the continuous phone calls to my cell phone and even my home phone at any time of the day; with the same message over and over: Just get Hazel to apologise and everything can go back to the way it was. Her tone became more and more insistent and more intrusive, and later even took on an undertone of threatening to take Hazel to court for defamation of character. (Ironically, it was Hazel's mother who had been telling numerous friends and family members.) Hazel's mother was more desperate than her father, and she had no intention or willingness to listen to or consider Hazel's experience. As far as she was concerned, if Hazel wanted to make accusations, then she had to specify dates and specific memories – precisely what Hazel could not do.

At this point, dear reader, I would like to ask you: What do you believe? Having followed Hazel's whole life story and journey, do you believe that she was sexually abused by her father? At the end of the day, this is the question that you and I are confronted with: Can we really know without having facts or memories? That is the crux of the whole story. In this scenario, there are no fence-sitters: either you believe Hazel's knowing or you don't; either you trust and believe her, or you don't.

The threat of a court case threw me into a state. How do you defend a case that is based on believing and soul-knowing, in a system that asks for evidence and facts? Panic set in. In my mind's eye, I could see a lawyer asking me questions and me providing answers that I knew would be laughed off in a court of law:

"Yes, your honour, but I know, deep down in my soul; I know Hazel has been sexually abused by her father."

"No, your honour, I can't tell you exactly how, or when, or where."

This would be followed by the defence lawyer's response:

"So let me get this straight: you believe it was Hazel's father because of a letter written in therapy twenty years ago and some dreams Hazel's been having?"

"No, it's much more complicated than that. There has been a history of behaviour, choices of partners, dissociations, hysteria, dreams of a sexual nature over an extended period of time, writings, unnatural responses of her body to sexual intercourse, and overwhelming reactions to normal everyday incidents such as her husband drying her son's private parts or her son pulling on her pants."

"Yes, but in what way does that implicate her father?"

"The soul knows."

"Say again?"

Then I would be forced to answer in facts:

"Well, your honour, dissociation is an abnormally strong psychological reaction to someone. Dissociation is not a natural response and only occurs with deep trauma. It happened to Hazel on more than one occasion with her father; and only with her father."

"Can you be one hundred percent sure it was her father?"

"No, I can't. But Hazel can; without facts. Your honour, have you ever come into a room and known, just known, deep down, that you have a strong connection with someone? Or have you ever had a deep urge to phone someone, and when you did, that person was having a particularly bad day or had important information for you, just at that time? How did you know? There is no proof to this knowing. We know, but we seldom listen to this knowing. Even if there had been the slightest doubt to Hazel's suspicions about her father, she walked away with a deep knowing after having confronted him. You can ask how she knew; I don't know how we know these things, but I know we do."

Apart from experiencing fears about a possible court case, I knew there was no way that Hazel's mother would understand and let things go. At the back of my mind, I did wonder whether it was in her interest not to understand; to ensure that doubt and even chaos reigned, so that attention would be placed elsewhere. I remembered the few implications that had come up in Hazel's dreams and had been portrayed in her childhood pictures; implications that Hazel's mother not only knew about her being sexually abused, but that she had been involved in some way.

Hazel had grown tremendously over the previous two years. Her healing journey was phenomenal. For the first time, I became aware of a shift in our relationship. As I was starting to get flustered about threats of court cases and what felt like constant badgering, Hazel for the first time took the lead in our therapeutic relationship. She started to support me and dealt with her parents in an admirable way, sticking to her truth while still allowing her parents to believe what they wanted; owning her own truth; and not allowing the chaos to cause doubt. Only when we hold onto a deep truth can we remain standing while the storms of life and family explode around us. Even more significant was the way in which Hazel managed things. We arranged a Skype meeting to discuss her parents' insistence on an apology. By that time, they were intruding severely into our lives. Hazel calmly spoke to them without being defensive. She again tried to explain to them what her soul already knew. Hazel explained that she was healing from the abuse and had made peace with her father; that she bore him no ill-will; but that she could not apologise. I was amazed and deeply moved. The shadow of a lady I had met three years previously at the Old Age Home was gone. Next to me in the Skype meeting sat a woman of gentleness and strength; the perfect balance of the two. I realised that this marked the beginning of the end of Hazel's healing journey. She would need this strength in what was the most difficult part still to come.

The Skype meeting did not resolve anything. After an hour of "Just apologise" and emotional intimidation and guilt-tripping ("Just see what you have done to your father"), we ended the meeting. The badgering continued, and soon the whole family was drawn into the chaos. Hazel's mother started to insist that Hazel had to be psychotic or mentally ill to have made such accusations and that she desperately needed therapy from a real therapist. She insisted that Hazel travel up to see her father's psychologist. Hazel's three brothers were pulled into the chaos and were soon choosing sides. There was even more pressure from different angles: "How do you know? Prove it was our father! Where is your proof? You can't make these accusations without a memory, without proof." The tape-recording of the confrontation was sent to everyone; this made some change their opinion around the situation, but not others. Phone calls were made backwards and forwards, and countless e-mails were sent and received.

After five months of family chaos, Hazel asked her father to go for a polygraph test to put the matter to rest. It was not the first time that members of the family had been asked to complete a polygraph test. When money had gone missing, a polygraph test had been done, and also when Hazel's mother had been accused of being involved in her brother, Mark's abuse (a test that she failed). I was astounded. "How strange for a family to resolve conflict with the results of a polygraph test", was the first thought that crossed my mind. It brought temporary calm to the chaos, as everyone waited for the test to be completed. A polygrapher in the town where Hazel's parents lived was approached. Initially he said he was not able to do the test, because there was no memory. Then, all of a sudden, he could do it. It was all quite confusing. He phoned Hazel and asked her for her definition of abuse, which she defined as "unwanted sexual touching"; however, in the test this was phrased as "raping".

In February, Hazel phoned, totally defeated. Her father had passed the polygraph test. The results of the test proved that her father had not sexually abused her. I was speechless. I could not explain it. Doubts started creeping in. Could it be possible that we had it wrong? I found myself going over the facts, the evidence, the knowing including Hazel's dreams, the automatic writing and the dissociations, over and over again. What had we missed? I spoke to Hazel again about her knowing, not only throughout her journey but also when she confronted her father. Hazel was devastated. Her anxiety returned. She also went through all the facts again and again. In the chaos, I consciously went back to the principles of psycho-spiritual intervention. I said to Hazel that we should trust her knowing and hang on to it. Often, reality requires us to choose between two options. However, in the spiritual world, paradoxes can co-exist, side-by-side. If we can hold the tension between what appear to be two opposites, the problem will become integrated – even if it appears impossible at first. There is a way in which both could be true; we just can't see it yet. I challenged Hazel to hold the paradox. I told her that we didn't have to choose sides or choose a specific truth for the moment. I encouraged her to try her best to hold the paradox – that both are true (the polygraph test result indicating that her father had not sexually abused her, but at the same time, the truth that she had been sexually abused by her father). We decided to focus on the tasks at hand. We continued writing, trusting that God would provide the answers when the time was right.

If we thought things were chaotic before the polygraph test, they escalated even more within Hazel's family afterwards. Expectations for Hazel to apologise became stronger, especially from one of her brothers. It's interesting to note that Hazel's father was never as insistent on an apology, even after the test results, as anyone else. Hazel went to speak to her parents, specifically her father, to acknowledge that the results baffled her and that she could not explain them. She did tell her father, though, that she had absolutely no certainty either way – whether he had definitely abused her sexually, or whether he had definitely not abused her sexually, and therefore she was not prepared to with-draw her accusation or to apologise. She also asked her father whether he could help her to identify who could possibly have abused her. His answer was "No" – just "No". He was not going to help. Hazel reiterated that she had made her peace with her father, despite what had happened.

Just typing this now, I am astounded at Hazel's maturity and strength and, above all, the serenity she displayed. Hazel knew that she had been sexually abused and she knew that her healing formed part of her life purpose going forward. She was holding the paradox. She still believed her soul truth but could acknowledge the results too. It was at that stage that I realised that I was not sure whether I would have been able to do it, and I told Hazel, "The student has surpassed the teacher." I was in awe of her healing journey and the person she had become. She had not only changed and healed; she had been transformed. Never again could she go back to being the bland wallflower that she had been two years previously. The signs were visible in other areas of Hazel's life as well. Her self-care improved. Her hairstyle changed; she was wearing her hair longer, loose, and in a more feminine, attractive style. Her clothing style changed. Her posture changed; she held herself more upright, with her head held high. She walked with more confidence. We laughed more during our sessions. Our discussions were less serious, Hazel was less anxious, and she focused on daily tasks and decisions that needed to be made. She hardly phoned me anymore regarding an anxiety-provoking moment. During difficult moments or decisions, she would meditate more, asking for spiritual guidance, and would then meet up with me to explain what had happened and what she had done. I became a witness; I was no longer her therapist.

We continued to write the book. Almost ten months after the results of the polygraph test, when Hazel started to write the chapter on the aftermath, she decided to look up a polygraph tester in town to enquire about the results. She had been living with the paradox for ten months but felt that she wanted to have answers to finish writing the book. This particular polygrapher is internationally renowned and one of the top polygraph testers in South Africa. He is also responsible for training testers nationally and has been approached internationally to help solve crimes. I asked Hazel whether I could come along. I was curious. I wondered how the paradox would be integrated. We took along the report of the results. He gave the results a look-over and assured us that they were invalid, and that further testing was required. He listed all the reasons:

i) The definition of the sexual abuse was too vague.

ii) Nowhere had names been used in the test – apparently the questions need to read something along the lines of, "Did you, Mr Lunderman, sexually abuse your daughter, Hazel?"

iii) Three questions needed to be posed for strong validation, but only two had been used.

iv) The report was only two pages long and did not include the actual results that were interpreted. (The industry standard is a five-page report.)

The polygrapher shared some of his own experiences in testing sexual offenders, and a discussion followed about Hazel's father's reactions around the confrontation and the test results. The polygrapher's opinion was that the test was invalid and therefore the results were invalid. We had our answer. What should have felt like a victory brought a sad realisation that this new information did not change anything about Hazel's family situation. Hazel said that she had come to the end. She did not wish to pursue the matter any further with a re-test, despite pressure from her family to do so. She wanted to continue with her life, finish her book, start her internship in play therapy, and fulfil her life purpose. She realised that her father was becoming frailer by the day, with more prominent signs of dementia, and she wanted the matter to be laid to rest. Her being right was not worth splitting up her family.

She knows her truth: She was sexually abused at a young age. The abuse was traumatic and, although she does not have a memory of the actual abuse, her body does remember in its reactions to unexpected incidents of a sexual nature. Her psyche remembers in the dissociations and in her dreams. The abuse affected her life for almost forty-five years, and it influenced so many decisions she made in her life, that she became a remnant of who she was created to be. Then she found the courage to start her healing journey. Along the way, she recovered lost parts of herself. She remembered who she is. She knows that she is never alone, as she has the lived experience of the guidance and protection from God and her guardian angel, even during the most trying times of her life. She has seen the universe conspiring to help her with synchronistic events. She found her life purpose. Hazel is not just a survivor of sexual abuse. Hazel is a spiritual being who loves, cares for, and will soon heal others. Now, after all we have been through, I can say that Hazel is a beautiful, strong and gentle spiritual being who happened to have been sexually abused. Her abuse no longer defines her. Ironically, the "who" of the sexual abuse is also no longer important now that she has truly been transformed.

READER'S REFLECTION:

Take a closer look at paradoxes in your life. Reflect on something in your life where you feel the need to make a choice between two seemingly opposite options. Visualise yourself holding an option in each hand. Just hold them and resist the urge to choose. Pray for guidance and then let go of the need to make a decision. When the time is right, God will show you a way forward. Go ahead and try it.

29

THE WAY FORWARD

Hazel

"The beauty of metamorphosing is not really about
becoming the butterfly, it's the lessons we learn
in the process of becoming ..." (Lynn Hill)

Joshua's play therapist's words to me when I left after my personal play therapy session with her spring to mind now as I
start to write this final chapter. Just before I closed the gate,
she said to me, "You will fly." Her words have been engraved into
my soul ever since that day. Intuitively, I knew that I needed time
to heal before moving forward onto the next phase of my journey
– my play therapy internship. Having nearly come to the end of
writing this book, I am finding the treasure of deeper insights
into the lessons I have learned through my healing journey.

The insight that forms the core foundation to all other aspects
of my healing has been the need to trust my own inner wisdom
through reconnecting with my soul and allowing it to open the
door to a much greater spiritual source of guidance and strength.
At my most critically challenging times, when my candle of hope
had almost blown out and there seemed to be no way forward,

I found my answers in the silent language of my soul. In this silence, I allowed my soul to become a channel for a greater, universal source of divine strength and healing. It was from this source that my answers came, usually in the form of songs or music. Sometimes the answers would come to me during or soon after specifically making time to meditate and/or work with my Oracle cards to connect with my guardian angel. However, mostly, in the busy rush of life (while driving to work, walking the dog, or emptying the dishwasher), I would simply ask my guardian angel to reveal a way forward to me.

Your greater divine source of strength and healing will be different from mine – maybe it is God, Jesus, Buddha, or the Lord. You will also have your own way of connecting to your soul – perhaps through prayer, contemplation, going to church, creative activities, or whatever feels right for you. Your soul will speak its own language – maybe not through songs, but through sayings, words, quotes, or pictures. You will learn to interpret the language of your soul, as you allow more time to listen to it. What is most important, I feel, is to try to incorporate it into your daily life in some way that works best for you.

My personal experience is that the more time I made for this, and the more I asked for help, the more synchronistic events flowed naturally into my life, providing signposts for the way forward, and offering healing. (Synchronicity is when two things, which seem to be meaningfully related to each other but have no direct cause to be linked, happen at the same time.) My most recent experience of synchronicity occurred when I meditated and asked my guardian angel for help with responding to my brother's reaction to my confrontation of my father regarding the polygraph test results. I chose three Oracle cards – "A New Dawn", "Rest", and "Synchronicity". Minutes after that, Louise sent me a message, saying that she was in the same area as Derrick, and asking whether I would mind if she spoke to him. The result was that Derrick and I managed to overcome some of our differences, and a barrier was lifted between us! So, as hard as it is, try to make time to listen to your soul and ask for guidance. Your answers will be given; perhaps not instantly and perhaps not in an immediately recognisable form, but they will be revealed to you.

I have also learnt that my soul will heal in its own time and at its own pace. Throughout the process of writing this book over the last four years, I have lived the insight I gained in the sand tray and through Edith's therapeutic story for me about the life cycle of the butterfly. The essence of it was that the butterfly's wings won't be strong enough to enable it to fly if it is assisted in hatching from the cocoon, because the hatching process is what strengthens its wings. If it is assisted, it will die because of its inability to fly. By allowing myself the time for healing through realising my dream of writing this book prior to moving on towards my internship, I have finally freed myself to heal more fully. Metamorphosis and birth are naturally independent processes and cannot be artificially interfered with by the mind. Personal transformation and healing have their own time frame. I finally feel that I am almost ready to be born as that butterfly with strong wings, and to fly into a future of healing others.

My healing journey has re-connected me to my personal strengths as a healer, but more specifically in the direction of healing others who have walked the same path as I have through the devastating trauma of sexual abuse. I always felt strongly drawn towards helping others through counselling and personal therapy, all those years ago as a Social Work and Psychology student. I lost sight of this, but as I started to heal myself, I found that people who didn't even know me started to share their stories of sexual abuse with me. As I started to receive more positive feedback from those sharing their stories with me, it both confirmed and more finely focused what I had lost sight of in myself. I have spent more than twenty years trying many different types of work including teaching young children, performing office/reception work, and working with the elderly. Finally, the most painful experience in my life is now bringing me the most beautiful gift – a pathway to follow towards using my personal strengths and living my life purpose through my work as a play therapist and counsellor. If you reflect on your most challenging life experiences and search deeply inside yourself, you too may be able to discover a gift that you have gained from them. Your deepest pain is often your greatest gift.

Furthermore, as shared in my chapter on Joshua, I have come to realise how our children often take us on the most important journey of our lives – that of healing our deepest wounds. They mirror our shadows, enabling us to embrace them and find healing. Have you ever wondered why your children are the experts at "pushing your buttons"? Perhaps, upon deeper reflection, you may realise that this ability of theirs has a purpose for you that goes beyond just pushing your boundaries with respect to discipline and shaping their wills without breaking their spirits. Does their ability to push your buttons shift and open your boundaries in a way that forces you to look at those parts of yourself that you would rather not see? Could it reflect your own hidden brokenness that got lost somewhere before your child came into your life?

One of my greatest sources of frustration is that I have never regained a conscious memory of my abuse. However, I am finally finding peace and healing, and have realised that these are not dependent on recovering a memory. I hope that some of my experiences shared with you in this book may be of help in your journey towards trusting your own innate capacity to heal, regardless of what questions remain unanswered for you. It is my experience that what you need to know, and what you are ready to know in order to heal, will be revealed to you. One of my greatest lessons was about finding peace with living with what I may never remember, as expressed in this book's title: *Too Close to Remember.*

In conclusion, in sharing my journey of healing with you, I hope, first and foremost, that I have inspired you to open yourself up to the greatest source of divine healing through listening to your soul. Secondly, for all you readers who may not have recovered a fully conscious memory of your abuse, I hope to instill a sense of trust that, despite this, you can still find peace and healing. Thirdly, for those of you who are parents, I want to encourage you to follow the signposts your children set before you that are leading you towards embracing your shadows, so that you can move towards potentially transformational healing. Finally, I would like to encourage you (both clients and therapists) to embrace the creative, therapeutic techniques explored on my journey – they are healing gems and can transport you to new levels of wholeness. These lessons have formed the very core of my healing process. They will also continue to form the signposts that I follow, directing me into a future in which I hope to be a tour guide for others on similar journeys.

My journey towards forgiveness and healing has moved me through denial, anger turned inwards in the form of depression, rage towards my abuser, overwhelming grief and pain, and finally towards a level of peace and forgiveness. I know that there is no shortcut to forgiveness other than through the pain. Finally, finding some purpose in my pain through sharing my journey with you by writing this book has been the most valuable part of my healing process. However, without you to read it and share my journey, this would never have been possible. Thank you for making this final stage in my healing journey possible by sharing it with me.

Reflecting now on mine and Louise's therapeutic journey together and the process of writing this book over the last four years, I have come to realise that they have formed just one chapter in the book of both of our lives. There are many more chapters to come for both of us as the ground starts to shift and we move into embracing new and exciting challenges ahead. When you are in your darkest moments of despair, it is often all too easy to lose this perspective – that the pain and darkness will form only one chapter of your life; you will heal and move into new chapters ahead.

Finally, I would like to leave you with a reminder of Joshua's words to me a while ago when we were talking about how we all experience God at different times and in different settings – for me, it was in nature. Having given him a few concrete examples and a short period of silence, he suddenly said, without any hesitation, "I can feel God now." When I asked him, "How does God feel to you?" he replied with the words, "Like I am flying". As children, we are more connected to our soul, more in tune with our own spirituality. I believe that, in the midst of our deepest pain, we all need to find and heal our inner child again. This will enable us to transform our broken wings and to come home to our soul.

In the words of Anna Bohlinger, "Pain travels through family lines until someone is ready to heal it in themselves. By going through this agony of healing, you no longer pass the poison chalice onto the generations that follow. It is incredibly important and sacred work."

EPILOGUE

Louise

We have come to the end of Hazel's healing journey. Her journey is not one of traditional therapeutic intervention, and there are numerous controversial aspects, even now at the end. If you are looking for evidence or a memory, there is none. I speculate that once Hazel becomes stronger and grows even more within herself, there is a chance that a memory may return in the future. As with Hazel's story, if you want life to make sense and have all the questions answered, you will be disappointed. Yet, having loose ends, questions that remain unanswered, and issues that are not all wrapped up, is probably a more realistic reflection of life. We experience unanswered questions when relationships end, and loose ends when people die without relationships being healed; sometimes life changes without there being a full stop or comma.

If you analyse Hazel's journey logically and view Hazel's recovery from a medical perspective, things will not add up or make sense. There is no logical explanation for the messages and insights she "received" during her meditations. No one can explain the synchronicities that happened after she asked for assistance from her guardian angel. The songs that came to Hazel all indicated important future happenings before the fact. Yet, psycho-spiritually, her recovery unfolded as it should have; exactly as it was meant to. I wasn't a traditional occupational therapist either. I just facilitated

Hazel's process, informing her of the psycho-spiritual principles and providing creative techniques with which she could recover her lost parts and reconnect with her soul. For the most part, I was a support, trusting her when she found it difficult to trust herself. At times, I was her witness when she blindly took a leap of faith; at other times, I just sat with Hazel and her emotions and accepted them all as gifts and messengers.

Despite Hazel's journey being unconventional, we have so much to learn from her story. Her story showed us the following:

- Our soul knows more than our thoughts. If we tap into our soul's wisdom, we will be guided to actions and insights we are not always conscious of.

- Anxiety and depression can be seen as messengers instead of symptoms of an illness.

- If we take one step towards God, God takes a thousand steps towards us, with synchronistic events meeting us in ways we could not even comprehend. It is almost as if God conspires to assist us. Yet, we need to take the first step, or rather leap of faith, to commit to our intention.

- When our actions are aligned with our soul and who we were created to be, we become more fully ourselves, and things start falling into place.

- We are never alone. God is always there, even if we don't feel or see Him, and our guardian angels protect and guide us every day if we allow them to.

- Trying to avoid suffering brings more suffering. When we embrace what is most uncomfortable or terrifying, something incredibly beautiful unfolds. In this way, our crosses become our salvation or, said in another way, our wounds become our redemption.

- Our aim in life is not to be perfect, but to be whole. In order to be whole, we need to embrace all our suppressed, dark, shadow qualities. The more whole we become, the more energy can be used to be who we were created to be, and the more liberated we become to live out our purpose.

- We are spiritual beings having a human experience, and nothing we do or say can diminish or enhance who we were created to be.

- There is no shortcut to true forgiveness, and forgiveness is a divine act that sets us free.

- Our soul's wisdom is more easily accessible than we think. We just need to become silent and listen.

- Creative techniques that bypass our defences and mind-chatter are effective techniques to use for accessing our soul. Each soul knows the way to its own healing and should therefore be accessed and provided with a voice within the therapeutic space.

- If we wait for the right time, the right partner, or the right job, we will be waiting for a long time.

- Nothing in life is coincidental. Everything in our past and our present is linked to our future.

- Our past, our brokenness, our shadows, our talents, and our character all work towards making us the ideal person to fulfil our life purpose. Your life purpose can only be fulfilled by you. Our life purpose is never in sole service of ourselves, but it is to enhance other people's lives.

- Our outside world reflects our inside world.

- Holding paradoxes allows our souls to integrate the seemingly opposite choices in creative, never-before-thought-of ways.

- Endings are not always neat boxes with bows, in which all loose ends have been tied.

Hazel has lived these truths. If these truths brought her to a place of healing, they could help you on your path towards coming home to yourself.

This journey started more than 20 years ago for me. I intuitively knew that God and our spirituality are needed for us to be healed and not just cured. I just didn't know how. I wasn't sure what the therapeutic journey would look like and what my role as therapist would be. In hindsight, I have seen God's hand in my journey: in my training as an occupational therapist; in leading me into the field of mental health; in the books that found their way to me, informing my thoughts and questioning my training; in the people that came into my life and questioned what I took for granted; in my search for a deeper meaning; in leading me to pack up and leave the city for the solitude of a rural environment; in my development of our St Raphael's Sanctuary Healing Retreat; and in its impact on my own life.

After all of that, Hazel came into my life – without fanfare; in a quiet, unassuming way. It's actually scary to think what I would have missed had I not answered the divine nudging I received. I took a leap of faith, without knowing where exactly we were going, and my eyes were opened. Initially, I theorised, speculated, and rationalised. However, the experiences were so much more: more exhilarating, more confronting, more disturbing, more overwhelming, more sacred, and more awe-inspiring than I could have imagined. I came to this journey trying to find *the* answer that could heal other people. I came away after Hazel's first St Raphael's retreat in a crisis: disillusioned, doubting, and disturbed. I was brutally confronted with my own shadows – not knowing, feeling powerless, and not being able to take away someone's pain. Those were my demons that came to confront me. They cajoled and mocked my idea of a therapist, of a healer, and of a helper – all roles with which I defined myself. They were the driving forces in my profession as an occupational therapist and in my twenty -year search for answers. I realised how many of my personal relationships had been initiated due to my wanting to help or fix people. Who was I without these? This small question belied the anguish I felt as I wrestled with this crisis. If I couldn't heal and fix, who was I? What was I supposed to do?

I now realise that part of my life-long search was coming from a place of my own fear of suffering. On reflection, I realise that my drive went even deeper than that: if I could find the solution to suffering, then by inference I could find the cause, and then I could end it or, even better, prevent suffering ... not only other people's suffering, but also my own. However, my "answers" did not hold healing. Onslaught after onslaught, Hazel was dumped into an ocean of suffering. I had no solutions, no answers. At times, all I could do was embrace Hazel with love, physically, emotionally, and spiritually – at times from a distance. I sat with her in moments of pain when it felt like the pain was going to overwhelm us both. At times, I was angry at God, wondering why Hazel needed to endure so much, when my life seemed relatively free of suffering, compared to hers. I felt that I was no more deserving than her, and I felt guilty that my life was blessed. I reasoned that if I could stop her pain and other people's pain, then maybe I would become worthy of my blessings.

It took my participation in Hazel's journey for me to realise that I need to let go of trying to fix pain and trying to end suffering. I found a quote by Maryam Hasnaa that summarises my new insight about healing and my role as a therapist: "A healer does not heal. A healer is someone who holds space for you while you awaken your inner healer, so you can heal yourself."

Coming away from this psycho-spiritual journey, I realise that God has all the answers. Ultimately, I don't understand many things around the issue of human suffering. I probably never will. What I do know is that, irrespective of how deep our wounds are, God never abandons us, and He is our Great Healer. I have also come to know two more things: Firstly, I realised that there is more value in suffering than what our western society would even consider to be true. As a society, we would do anything to avoid suffering and, in that way, we miss out on all the potential for transformation and all the gifts it brings for us. Secondly, I realised that human love is able to transcend all suffering. Despite the suffering described in this book, Hazel was surrounded and supported by those who loved her unconditionally: her husband Richard, their son Joshua, and her brother Mark. At the end of the day, love is more powerful than any suffering we will ever endure. May love uphold you in your darkest moments.

I would like to end with one of my favourite quotes by Teilhard de Chardin: "Someday, after we have mastered the winds, the waves, the tides and gravity, we shall harness for God the energies of love. Then for the second time in the history of the world, man will have discovered fire."

RESOURCES

Louise Fouche and the Family of Gentle Healers are here to support you on your healing journey.

You can connect with us in various way below:

Follow us on Facebook: Family of Gentle Healers: bit.ly/39D1bzv

Join our free Facebook Group, Soul Seekers Sanctuary: bit.ly/3mdPR4D

Visit us at www.FamilyOfGentleHealers.com

ABOUT ST. RAPHAEL SANCTUARY

The St. Raphael Sanctuary blossomed out of our family's passion for healing. It is our mission to guide people to heal, so they can experience what it feels like to be God's beloved.

The gap between psychology and spirituality must be bridged for true healing to occur. We, at the St. Raphael Sanctuary, have developed a unique psycho-spiritual approach for people suffering from mental and/ or spiritual dis-ease. Through our process, we guide participants to make sense of their suffering and to find hidden gifts in their pain and wounds.

St. Raphael's Sanctuary Healing Retreats, presented by our Family of Gentle Healers, are hosted on our farm, in Tulbagh, South Africa. Our family is made up of Father Albert, a Diocesan Catholic Priest, Louise an occupational therapist that specializes in mental health, Mimi our mother and prayer warrior, and Dr. Eric, a medical doctor. We have combined our accumulative 60+ years of experience and skills to make it possible for you to be able to overcome a range of obstacles and learn to make spirit-filled choices to live a passionate, joy-filled, extraordinary life.

We would be honored to accompany you on a journey so that you can heal your soul and find your true self.

To discover more information about our upcoming healing retreats and online programmes, go to www.FamilyofGentleHealers.com.

"I myself, with another priest, took part in some of the sessions and found the therapy methods used at St Raphael's Sanctuary most helpful.

I highly recommend this method/program of psychological and spiritual healing and find the methods and diagnosis used in agreement with the Roman Catholic faith."

Fr Colin Bowes
Priest and Diocesan Exorcist of the De Aar Diocese,
South Africa

ABOUT THE AUTHOR

Louise Fouché is the therapist at St Raphael Sanctuary and part of the Family of Gentle Healers. She is the founder of OTGrow that trains therapists in group therapy as well as in the psycho-spiritual approach to healing.

She is passionate about the spiritual and at the same time, the vulnerability and fragility of what it means to be human. She believes that it is through our brokenness that the light shines through. She says healing can only occur when our bodies-mind-soul is aligned and we experience acceptance and belonging.

She brings thirty years of experience as an occupational therapist specialised in mental health and a trainer, having trained more than 600 therapists to date. As an occupational therapist she makes use of creative therapies, so that clients can tap into the wisdom of their soul, which will lead them to find their best way to heal. She believes healing looks different for each person, because "we all have an inner guiding system, deeply connected to God, that shows us the way, if we will only pay attention".

Louise's vision is to train 5000 therapists who will value both the human and the spiritual in our journey towards healing and spiritual awakening.

Louise is situated on a beautiful farm in Tulbagh, South Africa called St Raphael's Sanctuary. She lives with her husband, Francois and her extended family who have been called to be healers, known as the Family of Gentle Healers. She has three independent children and she loves reading, hiking, being creative and hosting family and friends for any occasion.